THE OFFICIAL PICTIONARY® DICTIONARY

THE BOOK OF QUICK DRAW™

by Robert S. Angel,
Terry R. Langston
and Gary Everson

Illustrated by Clif Militello

A PERIGEE BOOK

Perigee Books
are published by
The Putnam Publishing Group
200 Madison Avenue
New York, NY 10016

Published simultaneously in Canada.

Library of Congress Cataloging-in-Publication Data

Angel, Robert S.
The official Pictionary dictionary : the book of quick draw / by Robert S. Angel : illustrated by Clif Militello.

p. cm.
Includes index.
1. Pictionary (Game)—Glossaries, vocabularies, etc.
I. Militello, Clif. II. Title.
GV1469.P52A54 1989 89-34961 CIP
793.73—dc20
ISBN 0-399-51578-X

Printed in the United States of America

1 2 3 4 5 6 7 8 9 10

For Bill—We all miss you.

Special thanks to:
Keith Corner, for giving us a running start
Sean Curran, for always being there to keep us on the ground
Emily Griep, for bringing order to our cluttered office

How to Use This Book

If you find yourself frantic for a good game of Pictionary®, but you happen to be alone or without a board game, or if you're playing and your teammates are stumped over a word—this handy little dictionary will ease the pain. Here's how it works:

Each page has ten sketches, representing two cards from the Pictionary® board game set. Each set of sketches has five blank lines underneath it, with categories in exactly the same order as the playing cards: Person/Place/Animal, Object, Action, Difficult, and All Play. You will see that the numbers in the upper corners of each page match the numbers in the lower left hand corner of the Pictionary® playing cards. For example, if your game card reads #32, you can flip to card #32 in the book and each word on the card is right there, described with a simple picture, in order of appearance. (A small number of earlier games do not have numbers on the cards. This will not affect game play.)

The *answers* to each set of sketches are found at the bottom of the following page, also listed by card number, printed very small so you can't peek. You'll find the answers to card numbers 499 and 500 on the bottom of sketch cards 1 and 2.

At the back of the book you'll find an index. All 2500 Pictionary® words are listed in alphabetical order, followed by the page number and that word's category. This way, if you're playing the game and you're stymied for a solution, you can flip to the sketch. REMEMBER: No cheating! You can only look up your word after your sixty seconds are up. You can then see what our artist did and remember the idea for the next time you have to draw that clue.

This book is designed to be played alone, like a game of solitaire, or with friends. To play alone, take one page at a time, try to guess the right words for the sketch, then record your answers on the lines below the drawings (we recommend using pencil). As in the board game, you are allowed more than one guess if you wish, and when you are through, check the small print on the following page for answers.

You can also play this book with others. Each player looks at a card of sketches and records his or her answers. Set a time limit if you like. Again, determine ahead of time how many answers are allowed. After each player's guesses are recorded, check the answers on the next page and keep a running tally of correct responses. The player with the most correct responses wins.

Don't forget—even if you've already filled in the answer blanks, this book makes a great reference for sharpening your Pictionary® skills. In case you've forgotten the rules of the game, we've included a quick refresher—as well as answers to the most commonly asked questions we've received from our players—in the next section. Read on.

Pictionary Rules

The object of the game is to identify through sketched clues as many words as necessary to advance to the finish square, and correctly identify the final word. Sketches may *not* include letters, numbers, or the # symbol.

To set up the game, position the timer and card box so all players can reach them. Divide equally into teams. Provide each team with a pad, pencil, category card, and marker. Place marker in the start square on the board. Each team selects a picturist—one who will sketch clues for the first word.

All markers rest in the P square to start, so the word in the P category is in play. The die is *not* rolled to advance at the start.

P—Person/Place/Animal (or related characteristics)
O—Object (things that can be touched or seen)
A—Action (things that can be performed, events)
D—Difficult (challenging words)
AP—All Play (this can be any type of word)

The starting picturist selects a word card and has five seconds to examine the word to be played. The timer is then turned and the picturist begins sketching clues for the team. The picturist may not communicate verbally or physically to teammates during the round. If a guess is correct, the team continues to play by rolling the die, advancing the number of squares indicated, and selecting a new picturist. THE PICTURIST POSITION ROTATES EVERY TIME A TEAM MUST SKETCH!

If a word is not identified within the time limit, the die is passed to the left, and the word corresponding to the square in which that team's marker lies is the word in play. A TEAM MUST OCCUPY A SQUARE AS LONG AS IT DOES NOT IDENTIFY THE GIVEN WORD.

In the All Play category, the word card is shown to the picturist of each team. The All Play word is sketched simultaneously by picturists to their respective teams at the start of the timer. *Regardless of whose All Play it is, the first team to identify the word earns control of the die and immediately rolls and advances the number of squares indicated.* This team now continues its turn with a new word. If no team identifies the word in the time allotted, the die is passed to the left. However, this team does *not* roll the die, but begins its turn by pulling a new card and sketching the word corresponding to the square they currently occupy. These rules apply when a triangle designates a word as an All Play.

In order to win, a team must reach the final All Play square. It must be the first team to identify the word in the same manner of play as in previous All Play categories. If it is, the team wins the game. If this is not accomplished, the die is passed to the left, or to the team that first identified the word. A team that reached the final All Play square cannot win the game by winning a round controlled by another team. It must first regain control of the die to attempt a winning word.

The number of players per team may be uneven if an odd number of players wish to play. In the case of three players, two teams are formed. One person must act as picturist for both teams. This person selects word cards and sketches throughout the entire game. THE PICTURIST MAY NEVER VARY. Normal game rules apply.

How precise an answer must be is up to the teams playing and should be decided at the start of the game. For example, is "robe" acceptable for "bathrobe"? "Combined" for "combine," or "Hope" for "Bob Hope"? The next section contains a list of the most commonly asked questions we've gotten from players.

Most Commonly Asked Questions Concerning Pictionary Rules

Q: During an All Play, do we get a full 60 seconds for each new word, or do we sketch as many words as we can in 60 seconds?

A: Every time a player pulls a new card, the timer is flipped. In an All Play situation, when a word is correctly guessed, the winning team pulls another card, looks at it, and then flips the timer over for another 60 seconds.

Q: What symbols can be used?

A: All symbols except the # can be used. Therefore, everything else is legal. Dollar and cent signs, mathematical symbols, arrows, etc. are all o.k.

Q: Can I use an "X" in my drawings?

A: Only to cross something out, or to indicate an area of a drawing. An "X" is never to be used as a letter, like in "x-ray" or "brand X."

Q: Can I erase?

A: Sure.

Q: Am I limited to one sheet of paper?

A: Nope, as many as you like.

Q: Can I look at the other teams' sketches?

A: Technically, you should look only at your own teammates' sketches. However, we realize this is hard to control. Before a game starts, decide if this is allowed.

Q: Do I get to roll the die when our team wins someone else's All Play?

A: Yes. Every time a word is correctly guessed, the die is then rolled by the winning team. If no one gets the word, whether the word is an All Play or not, then all playing pieces remain where they are and a new card is pulled. The square that is currently occupied is then the word to be drawn.

Q: What about making dashes like in Hang Man to indicate the number of letters in the word. Is this o.k. ?

A: No, it takes the fun out of the game.

Q: Can our team draw secret, or prearranged symbols to give clues, like "sounds like," or the number of syllables in the word, or if the word starts with a vowel or consonant?

A: No. The most common illegal act Pictionary enthusiasts perform is drawing an ear to indicate a "sounds like" word. This is not allowed.

Q: When we land on an All Play square, can we choose the word we want to draw?

A: No, you draw the All Play word. Similarly, when you land on a word preceded by a triangle, this word is sketched.

Q: How close does a word have to be? Can I say "teapot" for "tea"?

A: This is pretty much up to the individuals playing, but this is how we do it: If the word is "ice" and someone guesses "iceberg," that is not acceptable, because iceberg is one word. However, if a teammate says "ice cube," it's o.k. because that guess is two words. If the word is "tea," "tea bag" is o.k., but "teapot" is not. "High school" is all right for "high," but "highchair" is not.

Q: What about plurals and past tenses? Can I say "ran" for run, or "baked" for bake, or "hands" for hand?

A: Again, this is up to the people playing, but be sure to decide this before a game starts. When we play, though, we say one must guess the word exactly.

Q: What about hand gestures or signals?

A: Absolutely not.

Q: Can I use homonyms? If the word is "blue" can I draw "blew," or can I draw "weight" for "wait"?

A: Yes, as long as the pronunciation is the same.

Of course, if you and your teammates come up with great drawings from your board game, we'd love to see them. Send them to us (don't forget to include your name and address) and they just might make it into our *Book of Greatest Sketches*. Here's our address:

Pictionary, Inc.
P.O. Box 9907
Seattle, WA 98109

Upon submission, sketches become the property of Pictionary, Inc.

The Story of Pictionary

Rob

The sweat was starting to run and I hadn't even found a parking spot. I was wearing my entire dress wardrobe; one navy blazer—wool, one pair of gray slacks—wool; and one striped tie—ugly. It's not supposed to be so hot in Seattle in the month of May, I remember thinking.

This was two days before the grand opening party for Pictionary, the original charades-on-paper game; my partners and I still didn't have a store where we could send people to buy our game. I began to run through the spiel for the first Pictionary sales appointment in my head, but, on the way to the buyer's office, realized I had no product to show—no game, no order forms—nothing. In fact, I didn't even have the keys to my car, the one that was locked with the keys in the ignition. The one with its motor still running.

At that point, I decided I had two choices: I could laugh or I could cry. Sweating heavily and laughing my head off on the street corner in wool clothes, I rattled every lock on my junky, white, four-door Mercury Monarch. For some inexplicable reason, one of them opened.

When I got there, I was very warm. I'd run through my speech a hundred times and I was expecting some BIG desk in some BIG room. So, when I met the buyer on the sales floor and she asked, "Whaddya got?", I said, "Well, where are we going to go talk?" She looked around the store like a battle commander and said, "Perfume counter."

I followed her over, set up the game next to bottles of body splash and jars of wrinkle cream, and buzzed through my speech.

She looked right into me and said, "How much?"

I said, "Fifteen dollars."

She said, "How are they packed?"

I didn't even know what packed meant, so I said, "Uhhhhhh-mmmm, six!"

She said, "How much is freight?" not realizing that "freight" referred to my car.

"Uhhhhh, three dollars!" I said. I was making it up as I went.

She drilled me with another one. "What's your advertising allowance?" a term I had *never* heard in my life. So I fired back, "What's normal?"

She said "Ten percent."

I echoed "Ten percent."

In fact, I later learned that an advertising allowance is normally less than half of that amount, but what did I know then?

She said, "Okay, I'll take six."

Six! And suddenly I was setting up our first account. I couldn't believe it. I got out the new order forms that one of my business partners had created, and quickly realized that I didn't know how to fill it out.

The buyer looked at me, visibly shaking with excitement, and said, "Give me the pen." She filled out the order form for me, told me which carbon to take, and said, "Just ship me the games. See you later."

Fourteen million games and four and half years later, Pictionary practically sells itself, and I've tossed the ugly tie.

The seeds for Pictionary were sown in the shag carpet of a house I shared with three old friends in Spokane, Washington, after finishing college. I was a waiter at the time. My roommates and I used to hang out at home after work, sketching clues to one another from words we had pulled out of the dictionary. As soon as we began to play, I saw the potential of this game idea.

This charades-on-paper game became my entrepreneurial dream. With a supportive nudge from a friend, I scratched out some notes on a yellow legal tablet about how such a game should be played, and put together a short list of usable words.

Two and a half years later, after moving to Seattle, I found those old pages of game notes. At that time, Trivial Pursuit was one of the hottest-selling items in the country. This was all the inspiration I needed to move my game from the back burner to the front burner of full development.

I was still waiting tables, but I used my free time to read *every* word in the dictionary. At parties, I got friends to sketch the words I chose, gradually building a set of rules and usable words around the idea of Pictionary.

The next thing I needed was a design for the game, and a marketing plan, so I tapped my "professional contacts." I asked another waiter acquaintance, who knew graphics and printing, to wing it with me. I couldn't pay anything up front, just a share of the money if the project took off. This fellow waiter, Gary, didn't know a good deal when he heard one, so he took it.

Terry

I made a similar stumble into the game project. At the time, I was a serious CPA and avowed game hater, but I happened to land at one of Rob's playtesting parties, and got stuck on his Pictionary team. To say that we were terrible drawing partners is an understatement. We still are.

Though I didn't win at Pictionary that night, I had a great time playing it . . . and I hated games! So I figured if *I* liked this game, then we could probably get a lot of other people out there to like it, too.

I got a speeding ticket on the way to our first business lunch. Was this an omen? Our lunch lasted three hours and our conversation centered on how we would go about setting up a business. After that lunch was over, we knew something had to be happening.

Something was definitely happening that winter, but like the science projects that turn up in the back of the refrigerator, what resulted was not easily identifiable. Our relationship still defies description, but the three of us who fell into the game business together now call it Pictionary Incorporated.

Early in 1985, we borrowed $35,000 in start-up capital from Rob's aunt Ann and uncle Jerome Angel to produce our first 1,000 games. Jerome's accountant said emphatically, "Don't do it," but our enthusiasm about the project absolutely convinced him to write the check.

Once the financing was secure, we needed to launch this gamechild into production. But how?

Rob knew all the parts we needed for the game, so he went straight to the Yellow Pages. First, he looked under "boxes," calling each place to see if they could make boxes for a board game. Then he looked under "pencils," "dice," etc.

The only timers we could find had to be ordered 6,000 at a time, even though we needed only 1,000 for our first run of games. After they arrived, I remember commenting to Gary, "Well, if the game is a bomb, we'll be set with a lifetime supply of Christmas presents."

Gary

Yes, there were budget constraints to consider, but we were fully committed to creating a high-quality game. We didn't want Pictionary to come off looking cheap or shoddy; it had to look good on a coffee table. I remember when we were choosing game markers; most are just hollow, junky plastic. We wanted something solid, yet simple, so I came up with the idea of using dice without the dots drilled into them. How much simpler could we get?

Having piecemealed the game together with services from nine different companies, one production detail remained—getting the sheets of game cards sliced and collated. Once we'd found someone to do that cutting and collating, we had just enough money left over to throw a grand opening party for Pictionary on June 1, 1985.

Rob

Gary sent out invitations; Terry hired a caterer. It was eight days before showtime. Then the phone rang.

A representative of the company that was going to cut and collate the game cards was calling. He tried to begin gently. "We've got a little problem."

I said, "Problem?"

The "problem" was an error in the time and cost estimations he'd first given us. The job was going to take twice as long to do and cost three times as much as he had originally said it would.

"No way. We don't have the money or the time," I screamed, and launched the phone across the room (that was the only tantrum I've ever thrown . . . well, actually the *first* tantrum).

If ever a Pictionary Hall of Fame is compiled, this moment will undoubtedly provide its starring member—Sean Curran. Sean is there when the phone went flying. Fortunately, Sean is the kind of friend who knew that this disaster warranted more than a shoulder to cry on. Within minutes, he laid out a scheme that would save our butts and get Pictionary back on schedule.

His plan began with a dive back into what had been my primary reference manual—the Yellow Pages—to find the tools we would need for collating.

Eight rented banquet tables and 170 shoe boxes later, my one-bedroom apartment was transformed into Pictionary's assembly headquarters. We moved everything out of the living room and into my bedroom. To this day it still amazes me that everything I owned fit into one ten-by-twelve-foot room.

The original printer of the game agreed to cut the monstrous sheets of cards. Then, all *half million cards* (500 per game) were sent to my apartment to be collated by hand; the "cottage industry" phase of Pictionary was under way.

My living room suddenly housed a complicated maze. The assembly line started at the front door of the apartment, snaked through the banquet tables in the living room, around the kitchen counters, back through the living room and kitchen to the front door. A person would grab a handful of cards and a checklist and work through the line of card boxes, putting a card in, checking it off, simultaneously dodging pizza cartons and beer bottles along the way.

For six days, sixteen hours per day, the four of us sorted cards, drank beer, sorted cards, ate pizza, sorted cards, and sorted cards. We also asked everyone we had ever known to come and do a sorting stint. Mirroring our own commitment to the game, many of our friends showed up.

The more we did, the more we thought we could sell at the grand opening party, which was less than a week away. So, a carload at time, we moved 175 games to the party site. One hundred and seventy-five games weigh about . . . oh, 1,200 pounds.

We sold forty-two.

It was like a big prom date that had bombed. We'd spent nearly a grand on that party—a grand we didn't have—*plus,* we'd forgotten to invite the press. *And* we only sold a quarter of all the games that we had eagerly lugged across town.

I think that's typical of us, though; we won't hesitate to spend money on a party to entertain *ourselves.*

GARY

Rob, Terry, and I were the entire distributing/marketing department for the first year. We physically peddled the game. We didn't have an advertising budget. We wore sweatshirts printed with the Pictionary logo everywhere and we just *told* everyone about it.

One of our marketing strategies included playing the game in public—at outdoor cafés, restaurants, or bars—and getting others to join in. We amplified our efforts by leaving a tangible reminder of the game with people. We handed out "pic-packs," a promotional item Terry invented. "Pic-packs" were a shrink-wrapped packet that included a pencil, a drawing pad, some Pictionary game cards, and a mini game board.

After the disheartening "forty-two debut," we launched a second mid-summer bash, specifically for the press. The media helped us tell even more people about the game. It worked. By Labor Day, many locals had heard of, and were hot for, Pictionary—the Game of Quick Draw. Our entire first run of games sold in only three months.

I think one of the reasons our sales were increasing, however, was due to my buying games—not exactly ethical, but pretty effective.

In fact, I bought only two games, but I definitely used some creative tactics to nudge the progress of the game along. A store near my home, for instance, had cautiously put six Pictionary games on the shelf. Each day after work I would check on their sales progress. Finally, in an attempt to get the store to reorder, I posed as a customer and plucked the last two games off the shelf.

I also called—repeatedly—every store that I knew didn't carry the game and said, "I played this great game, Pictionary, last night. Do you sell it? I can't find it anywhere."

I used to sneak Pictionary boxes from the lower shelves of stores to those at eye level whenever I could get away with it.

"In-store marketing," we call it.

TERRY

As the first 1,000 games sold out, and it began to look obvious that ordering a second run would be a wise move, there were still few people who took us seriously, including good friends, relatives, and co-workers. Bankers, of course, either laughed in our faces or politely said "Sorry, guys," when we went searching for money to secure that second order of games. Two potential venture capitalists even stood us up. And Gary's father once said to him, "Take a grand and get out while you can."

Once the first 1,000 had sold, we had just enough money in the bank to put a down payment on the second run of games. We wanted only 10,000, but we didn't think the new manufacturer would go for it, so we said 20,000 initially, hoping that by the time we signed the purchase order, we could talk them down to ten. It worked.

The one problem remaining, however, was coming up with the $80,000 balance by the time the production run was completed and ready to be delivered—in 60 days.

So we decided it was again time to test Uncle Jerome's commitment. Armed with detailed sales projections, more entrepreneurial enthusiasm and, coincidentally, hangovers, we laid out our plans to our investor.

He committed. We were on cloud nine, laughing like little kids. Then, as we drove out of the parking lot, we suddenly had to stop; we'd forgotten the stupid check!

* * *

Selling our game was an incredible rush. Unfortunately, adrenaline doesn't pay rent and phone bills. Every spare penny and ounce of energy we produced that first year went right back into keeping the business moving.

The early days of Pictionary's life were a blur. While Gary and I put in daytime hours at our full-time jobs, Rob went out to make sales calls and distribute games. At night and on weekends, we kept up a brisk business pace—typing invoices, setting up tournaments, demonstrating games, organizing finances, and losing sleep.

I remember falling into bed completely exhausted at 2 A.M. one night. An hour later, I was wide awake, realizing that I had to make a choice—keep my full-time job, or commit completely to this game. The next day, I went into my boss's office at a local high-tech company and quit.

After an equally exhausting two years of moonlighting, Gary called it quits on his nine-to-five magazine graphics job and hooked his future to Pictionary as well.

We realized that getting the pencil in people's hands was the key to selling Pictionary. Once they did, they were hooked. Hands-on, in-store demonstrations were really what did it for us, especially at Nordstrom, an upscale apparel department store that didn't even have a game department (until we came along).

We would go in during the holiday season, set up a table, and show people how to play the game. Sometimes as many as ten to fifteen people played at once. The players would be screaming and yelling, having fun trying to guess a Pictionary word, and it would create wonderful traffic jams. People wanted to see what the excitement was about.

Without question, those demos were our best marketing tool.

Rob

Early in 1986 I awoke to the sound of a clairvoyant's voice on a local radio show. On a whim, I called the station and said, "Hi, my name is Rob and I invented a game. How is it going to do?"

The clairvoyant said, "Rob, first I have to tell you to beware of the balding man. I see a balding man in your future; you should look out for him. But in the long run, I predict that you will be as popular as Cabbage Patch dolls."

She turned out to be right on both counts. Not long after her prediction, we were in the process of deciding on a national sales manager. It turns out that the person we did not choose was the balding man. The other, Tom McGuire, helped make our game the success it is today.

TERRY

In mid-1986, Tom McGuire was staring forced retirement in the face. A twenty-three-year sales veteran for Selchow and Righter, licensee of such games as Scrabble and Trivial Pursuit, Tom's future was being threatened by the doom of a buyout.

Tom knew that, because of his age, fifty-plus (and he won't tell you how much plus), he would probably be out of the picture at Selchow and Righter.

He'd heard that the "Pictionary guys," as he calls us, were looking for a national sales manager, so he applied for the job.

We looked at Tom's track record like casting directors scrutinizing a screen test. We liked what we saw in his game background, and our guts told us he was the right choice; so we scooped him up.

Once McGuire had signed on as our national sales manager, he invited four of his co–game veterans aboard. Pictionary's national sales zoomed, a blessing that created its own dilemma. In less than a year, 45,000 games had been sold. Suddenly, it was glaringly evident that we needed heavy capital to maintain production levels. That meant finding a company to license and produce our game; in other words, a company that would, by agreement, pay for manufacturing and distribution costs up front.

Ironically, one of the country's biggest names in games then came knocking on our door. Milton Bradley wooed us like a perfectly mannered suitor. Yet, as sweet as the courtship looked, a written licensing agreement between the big game folks and us remained elusive. We took a collective deep breath and politely said "no thank you" to Milton Bradley . . . to Milton Bradley!

The risk was haunting. We kept wondering "did we do the right thing?" But as we rank amateurs quaked in our boots, another deal was already in the works.

Joe Cornacchia, a respected game broker, was working out a custom-designed arrangement with a potential licensee for Pictionary. We signed an agreement with Cornacchia's new venture, Western Publishing/Cornacchia Press, giving us fuel to let sales go big fast.

Meanwhile, the trusted reps who composed the Pictionary sales force were teaming up to create an independent sales and marketing company, The Games Gang, Limited, also known as "the over-the-hill gang."

GARY

When we started this whole thing, all we thought about was Pictionary, blue box, first edition. Now a total of eight versions of Pictionary (first edition, second edition, Pictionary Junior, Bible Pictionary, Bible Pictionary Junior, Pictionary Junior-Play it with Clay, Travel Pictionary, Party Pictionary) fill store shelves, while a Pictionary game show recently debuted on national television.

On the international scene, Pictionary was dubbed Best Game of the Year for two consecutive years at the British Toy Fair, a feat previously unmatched. The Toy Wholesalers of America gave Pictionary the same honors—Best Game in '87 and Best Game in '88, another "never-before" in the toy industry.

Our game has been mentioned in novels, comic books, movie-star interviews. We're part of Americana, or, actually, part of the world. Pictionary is currently produced in fourteen languages and distributed in twenty countries.

If imitation is the sincerest form of flattery, then we've been flattered many times over. There are at least twenty-five copies of the Pictionary concept worldwide. But we, the creators of the *original* charades-on-paper game, say to our imitators, "It's not whether you win or lose, it's how you draw 'success.' "

You don't have to grow up to be in the game business; we prove it every day. The three rules of the Pictionary Office are:

1. The first person to the office in the morning is President for the day.
2. No ties allowed.
3. If someone is gone for more than a day, it is hoped they are having a good time—no questions asked.

Desks in our office are as likely to be cluttered with Ping-Pong ball guns as they are with business memos. The walls are not filled with sales charts or marketing reports. Instead, there is photo after photo of our smiling mugs. These pictures document the history of Pictionary: the annual "thank you" cruises, a birthday party, or an impromptu ski trip. There's even a photo of a business meeting with the Games Gang. It features Terry and Rob sporting silver-sprayed hair, so they could look just like all of our sales reps who were at the meeting.

If there were a Pictionary corporate philosophy, it would be something like "Go with your gut." We've done just about everything by gut. We've broken lots of the corporate world's rules . . . and it's worked for us.

Rob, Terry, and Gary

Pictionary didn't just fall together out of luck. The game has become a phenomenal success largely because we were willing to commit ourselves to a dream and to take risks. We started out five years ago not knowing exactly what we were doing. But we've created something that works for us. This is our business. It's our future.

We still work some weekends and put in late nights. Of course, it helps that we love what we do. We like to say that we're working our butts off for fun. These days, our challenge is to find the balance between the work and the play, and we are trying very hard to perfect both.

Do we claim any secret to our success? Yes. It's the fact that we take everything seriously, except ourselves. It is, after all, just a game.

—Jayme Lynes

499. Orphan, Jelly Bean, Behead, Venom, Drawbridge
500. Pluto, Faucet, Point, Import, Fireplace

1. Mae West, Pancake, Attach, Funny, Mosaic
2. Deer, Yardstick, Bump, Lad, Postage Stamp

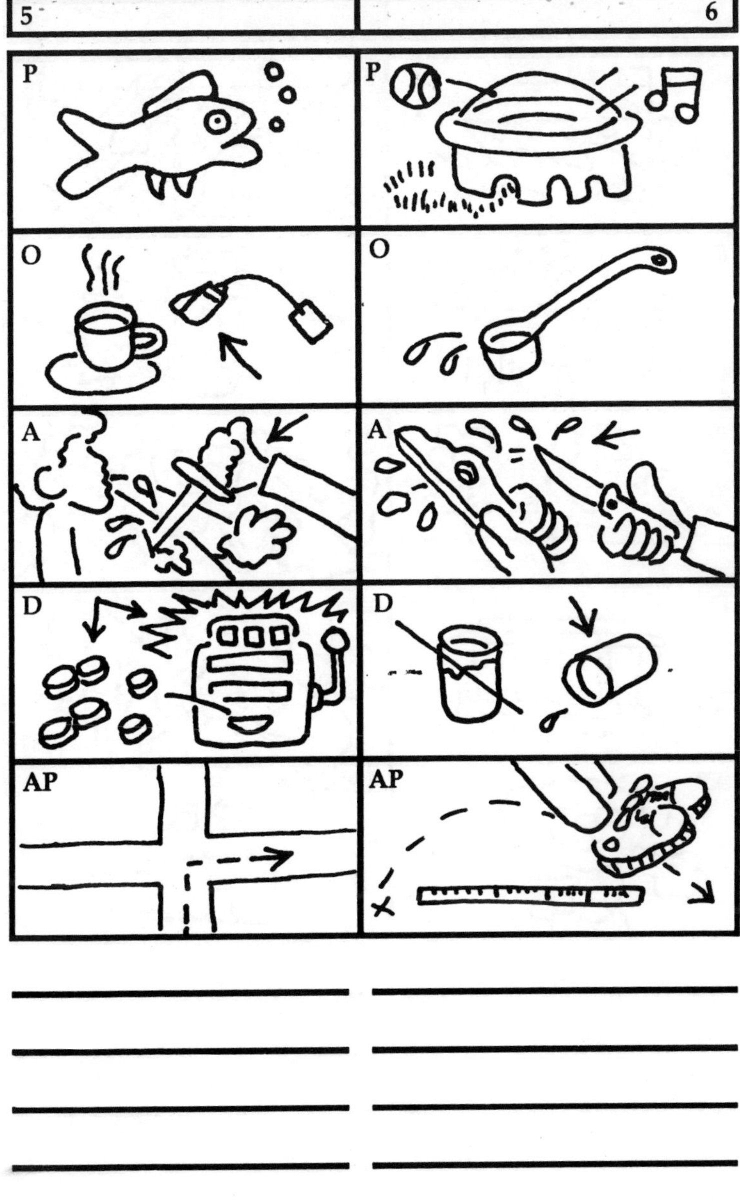

3. Texas, Checkers, Haul, Storm, Check Mark
4. Store, Noose, Embarrass, NASA, Space

5. Fish, Tea Bag, Stab, Jackpot, Right
6. Astrodome, Ladle, Whittle, Empty, Long Jump

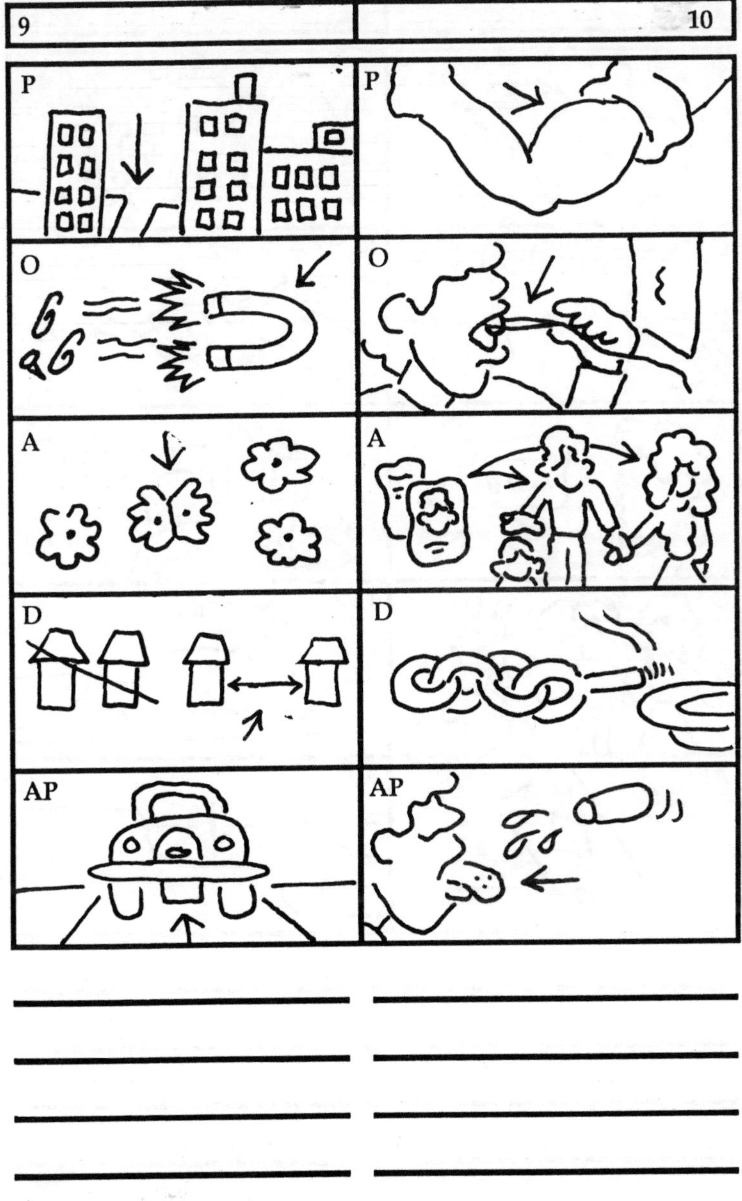

7. Ocean, Straw, Grow, Cable Car, Teddy Bear
8. Beach, Lantern, Talk, Medium, Chimney

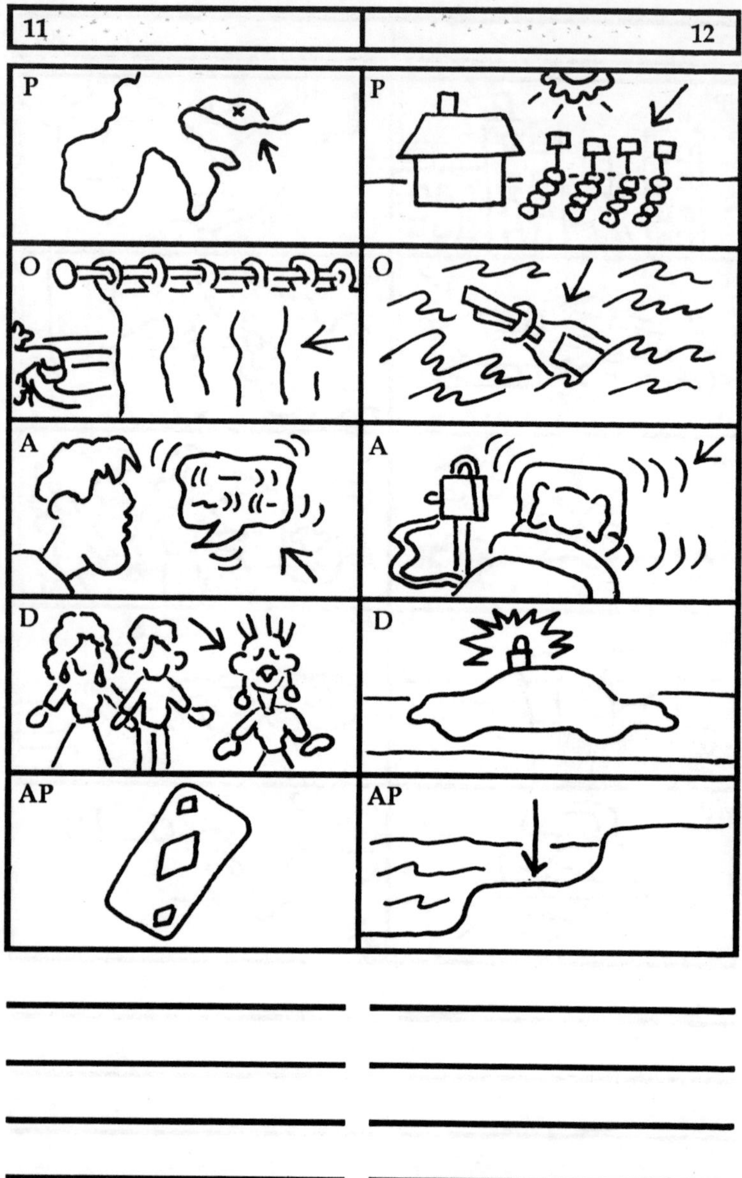

9. Downtown, Magnet, Split, Far, License Plate
10. Bicep, Dental Floss, Adopt, Chain Smoker, Taste Bud

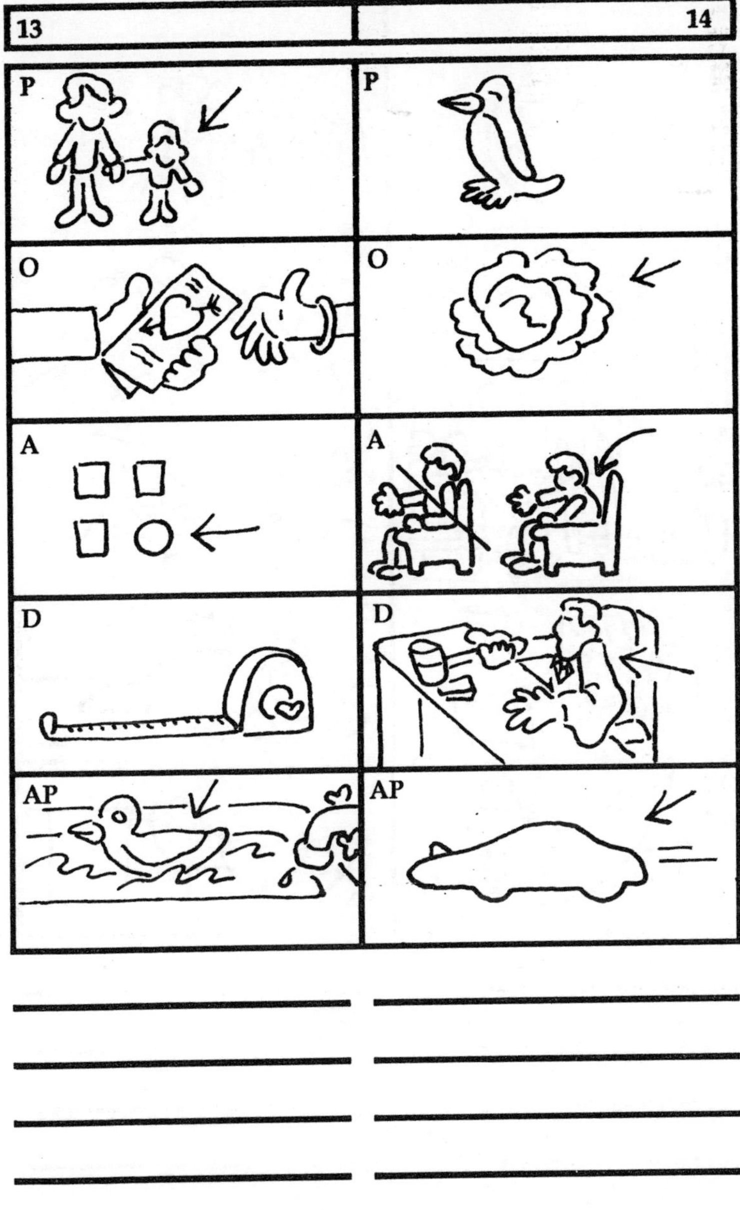

11. Yugoslavia, Curtain, Stutter, Teenager, Ace
12. Garden, Bottle, Vibrate, Police Car, Shallow

13. Boy, Valentine, Different, Tape Measure, Rubber Duck
14. Penguin, Lettuce, Slouch, Judge, Rear

15. Smile, Basket, Elope, Oxygen, Ski Jump
16. Cowboy, Baton, Flop, Caffeine, Large

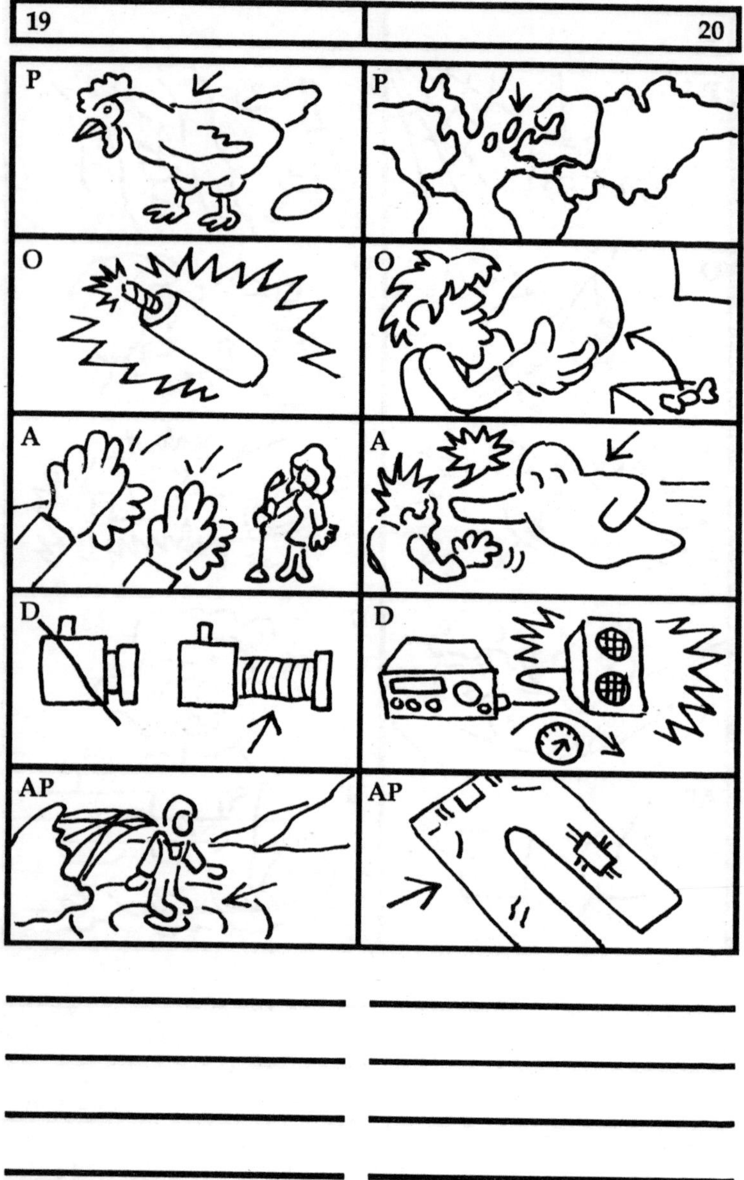

17. Spider, Grape Vine, Alarm, Pudgy, Square
18. Right Bank, Perfume, Blaze, Gap, Lifeboat

19. Chicken, Dynamite, Applaud, Zoom Lens, Land
20. British Isles, Chewing Gum, Haunt, Volume, Pants

21. Wrist, Motor, Tug, Civilian, Lung
22. Orchard, Stamp, Drill, Hard, Coin

23. Rat, Key Ring, Fetch, Blank Check, Sun
24. Black Widow, Radiator, Brand, Mayor, Bubble Bath

25. Mother, Pillowcase, Dip, No, Fat
26. Palace, Guitar, Clap, Gymnastics, Flood

27. Nile, Compass, Link, Witch, Launch Pad
28. Iowa, Suitcase, Time, Blind Date, Harness

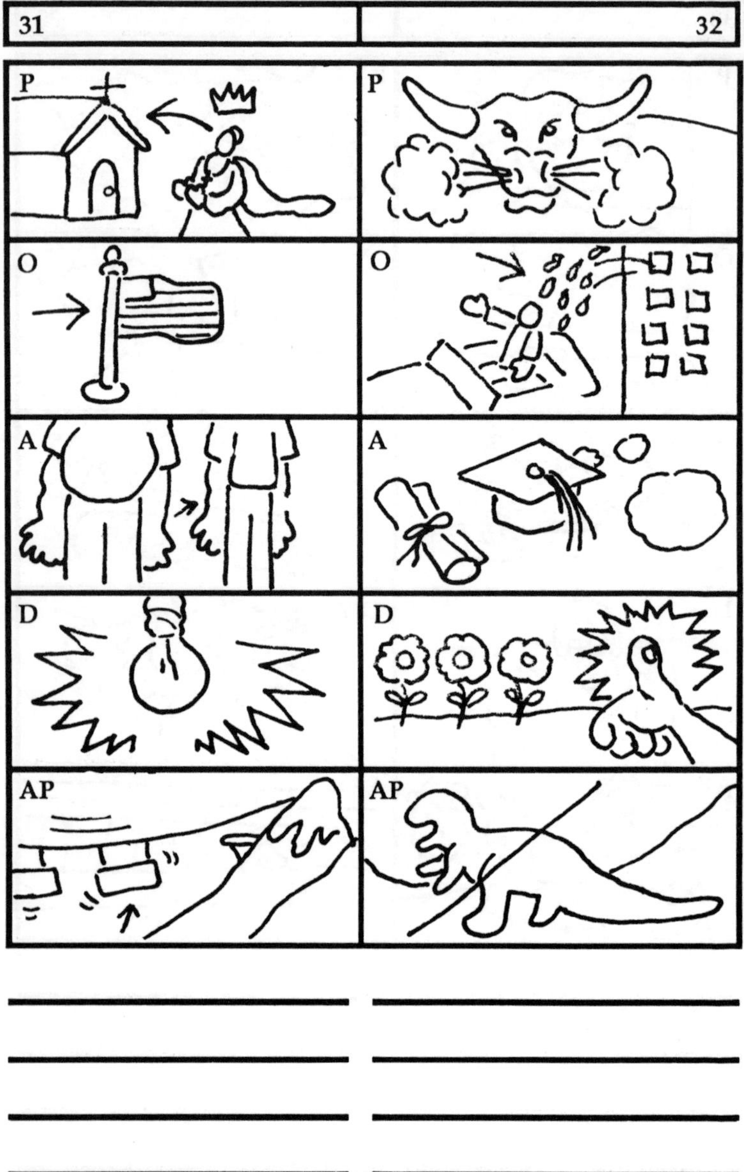

29. Eyelash, Airplane, Clamp, Shoulder Pads, Dehydrated
30. Senor, Ballot, Wrinkle, Ripe, Off-Ramp

31. Pope, Flagpole, Diet, Bright, Chairlift
32. Bull, Confetti, Graduate, Green Thumb, Extinct

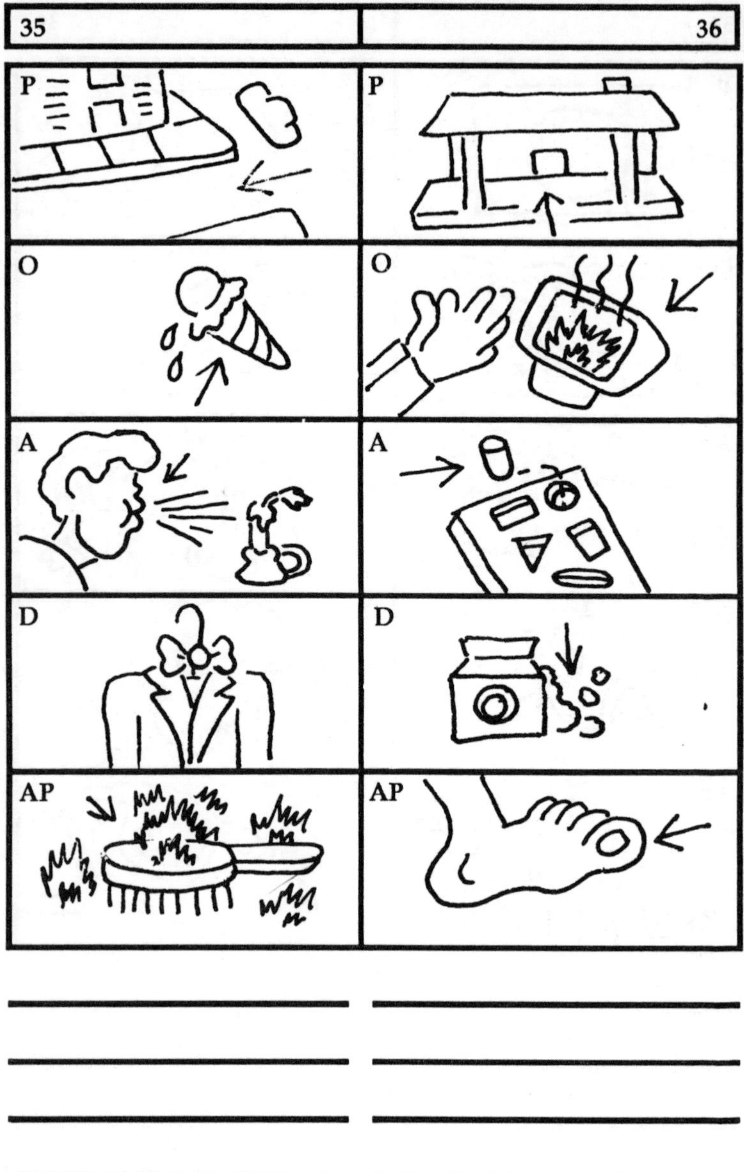

33. Japan, Coconut, Gaze, Happy, Mace
34. Oregon, Collar, Burn, Earwig, Gasoline

35. Street, Cone, Blow, Formal, Brush Fire
36. Porch, Heater, Peg, Suds, Big Toe

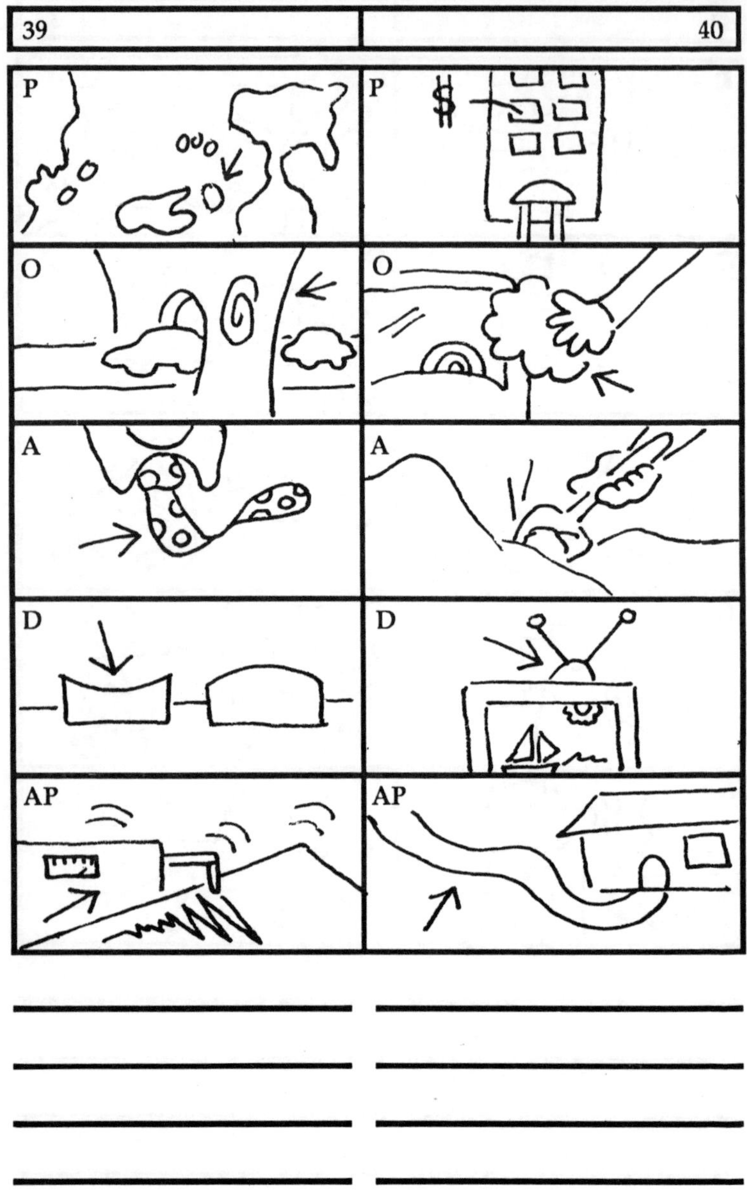

37. Desert , Desk, Bury, Rearview Mirror, Bad Breath
38. Delivery Room, Gurney, Sell, About Face, Star

39. New Zealand, Redwood, Tie, Concave, Richter Scale
40. Condominium, Rag, Dig, Rabbit Ears, Path

41. Hercules, Knife, Blink, Picket Fence, Pork
42. Rattlesnake, Porthole, Stumble, Darkroom, Hurricane

43. Bank, Goal Post, Phone, Cockpit, Four O'Clock
44. I, Anvil, Salute, Bum, Backache

45. Fisherman, Range, Waste, Loft, Weather Vane
46. Siberia, Hula Hoop, Grab, Matinee, Cable T.V.

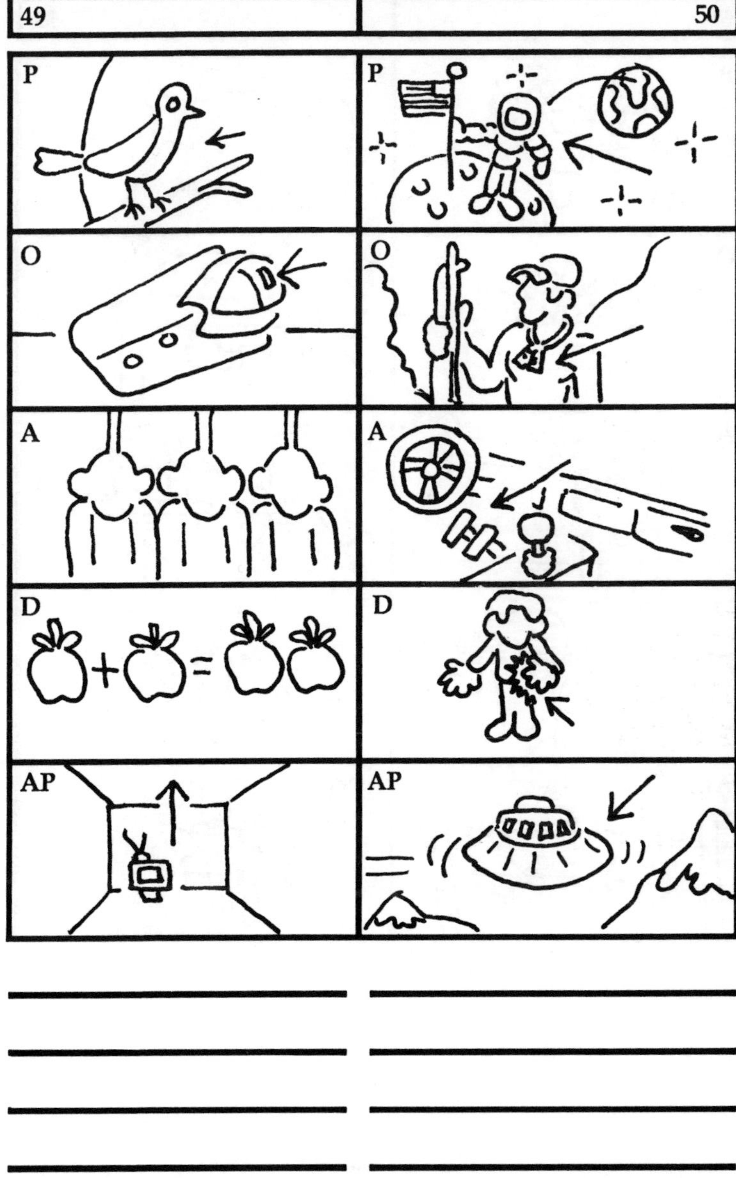

47. Sheep, Slipper, Frisk, Penitentiary, Vacant Lot
48. Baby, Nylons, Mount, Sweet, Ugly

49. Bird, Label, Clone, Math, Ceiling
50. Neil Armstrong, Dog Tag, Clutch, Side Ache, Flying Saucer

51. Stomach, Log, Pat, Translator, Barbwire
52. Massachusetts, Drainpipe, Align, Candlestick, Peg Leg

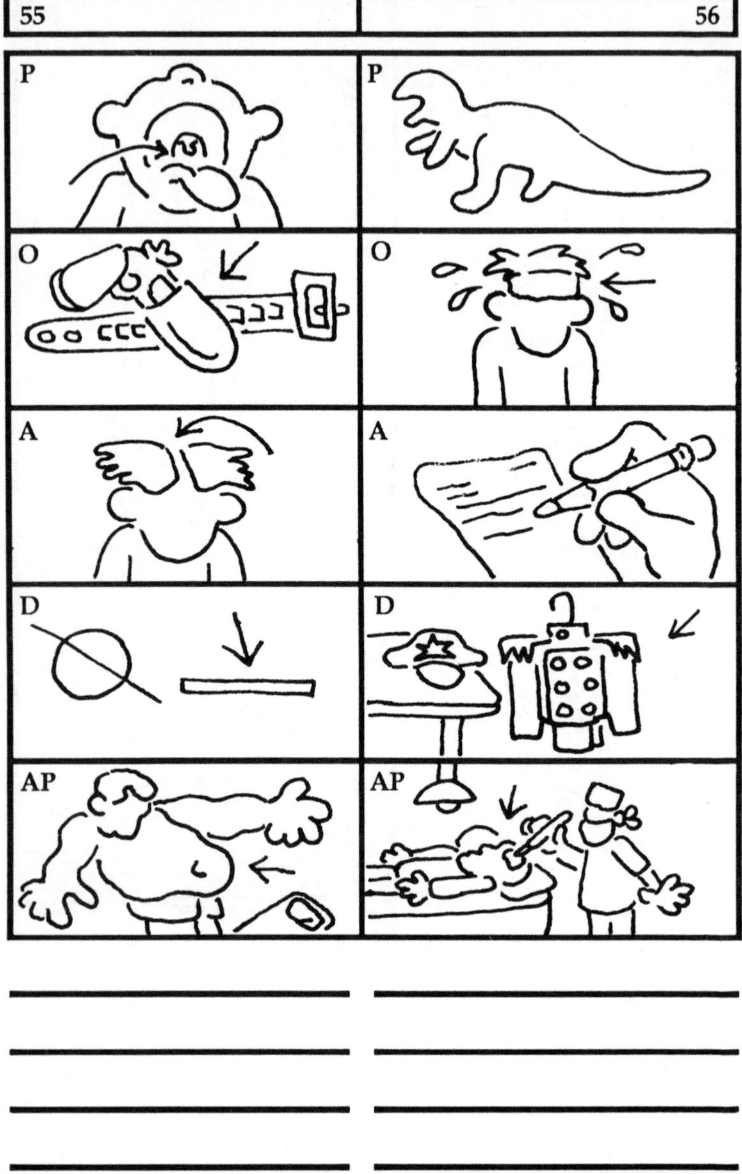

53. Dachshund, Spider Web, Gore, Behind, Dominos
54. Elephant, Strait Jacket, Die, Shuffleboard, Railroad

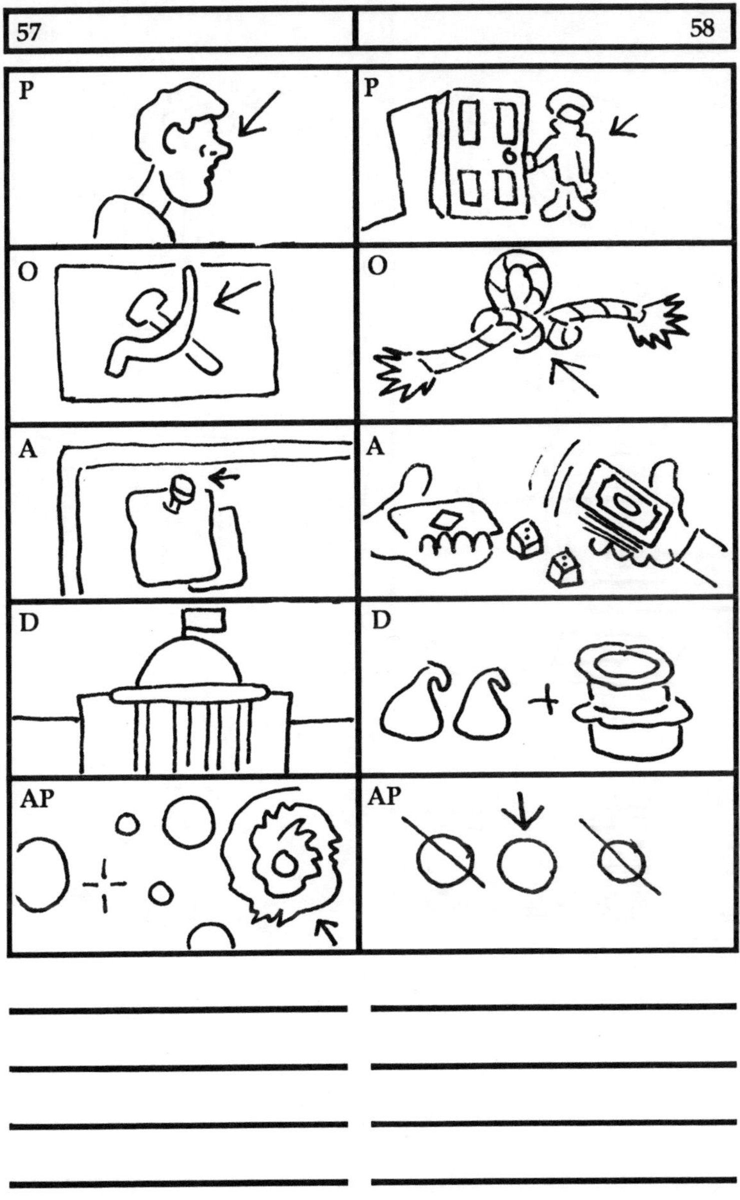

55. Tonsil, Holster, Part, Flat, Obese
56. Dinosaur, Sweatband, Jot, Uniform, Lobotomy

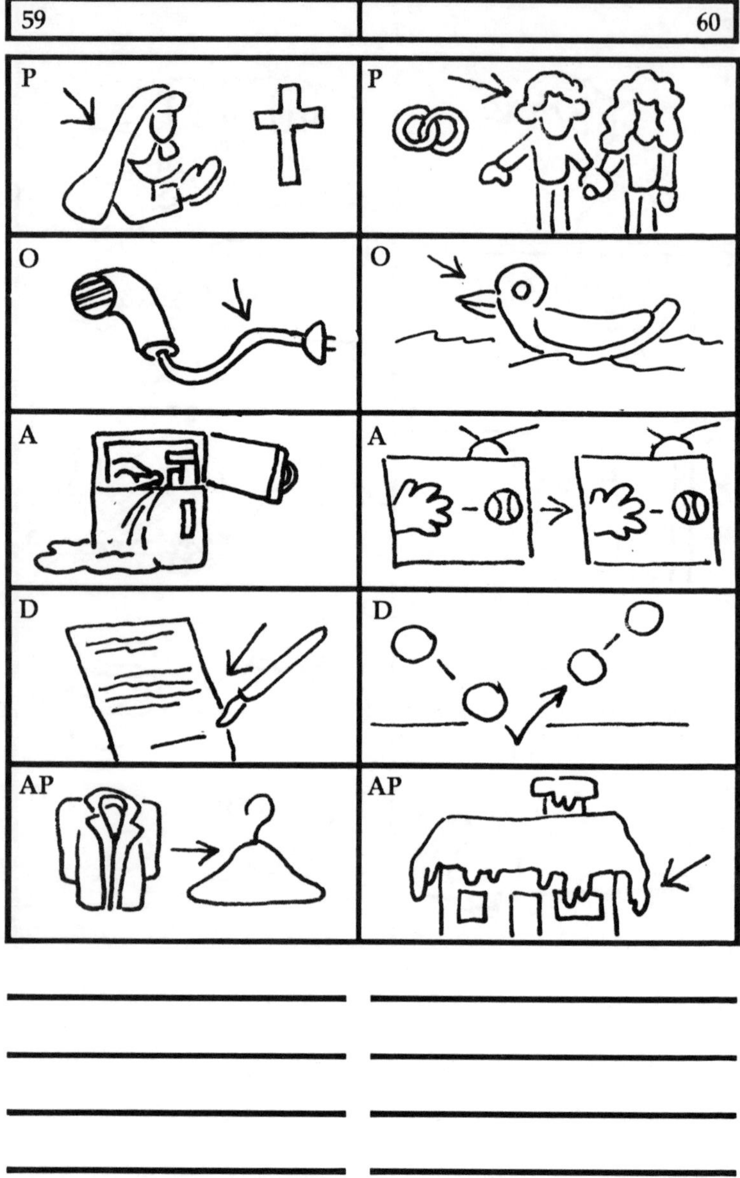

57. Nose, Sickle, Tack, Government, Black Hole
58. Doorman, Knot, Gamble, Chocolate Cake, Middle

59. Nun, Cord, Defrost, Signature, Coat Hanger
60. Husband, Bill, Replay, Rubber, Icicle

61. Man, Swim Suit, Retire, Telephone Cord, Stop Sign
62. Pasture, Salad, Debate, Time Zone, Dimple

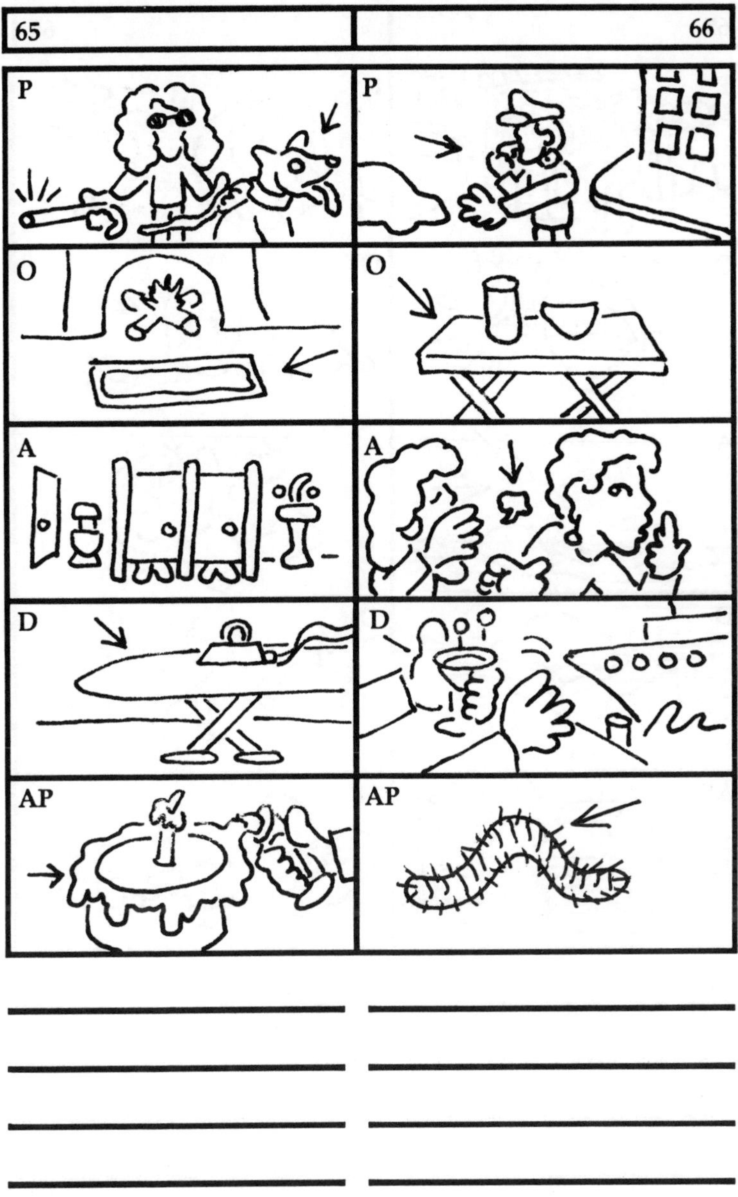

63. Upstairs, Bookcase, Draw, Scribble, Kiss
64. New England, Ladder, Rip, Pollen, Beak

65. Seeing Eye Dog, Rug, Occupy, Ironing Board, Frosting
66. Police, Tray, Whisper, Bon Voyage, Fuzzy

67. Villa, Diamond Ring, Mop, Tissue, Low Tide
68. Earth, Costume, Drink, Coffee Table, Glue

69. Lobby, Engine, Sand, Pigpen, Appendix
70. Deck, Discus, Kidnap, Pineapple, Cyclone

71. Panama Canal, Luggage, Row, Pudding, Period
72. Race Track, Rowboat, Sing, Cove, Mouthwash

73. Index Finger, Slingshot, Beat, Turntable, Cymbal
74. San Francisco, Lollipop, Think, Near, Upside Down

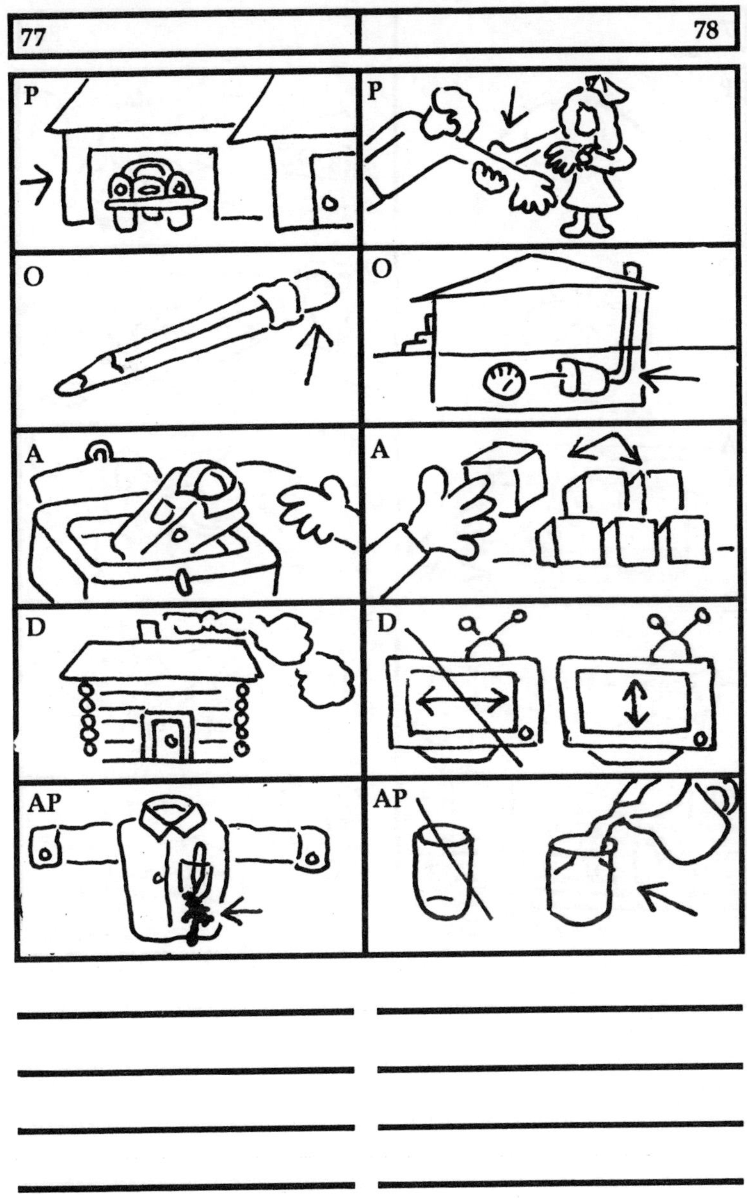

75. Hickey, Derringer, Whistle, Bicuspid, Saliva
76. Hawaii, Hurdle, Frame, Cheeseburger, Tidal Wave

77. Garage, Eraser, Pack, Log Cabin, Stain
78. Pulse, Furnace, Build, Vertical, Full

79. Eye, Berry, Blast, Peanut Butter, Garbage Can
80. Mouse, Ticket, Erupt, World War I, Visor

81. Wart, Stereo, Unveil, Escape, Morse Code
82. Bathroom, Ashtray, Alter, Gobble, Mermaid

85	86

P	P
O	O
A	A
D	D
AP	AP

83. Right Hand, Wrist Watch, Nose Dive, Wall-To-Wall, Honeymoon
84. Woodpecker, Outlet, Unwrap, Rotten, Lamb

85. Motel, Puppet, Shove, Pastry, Outer Space
86. Idaho, Sign, Unclog, Bookmark, Well

87. Wisconsin, Dock, Notch, Etch, Poll
88. Conductor, Tablespoon, Ripple, Tennis, Ship

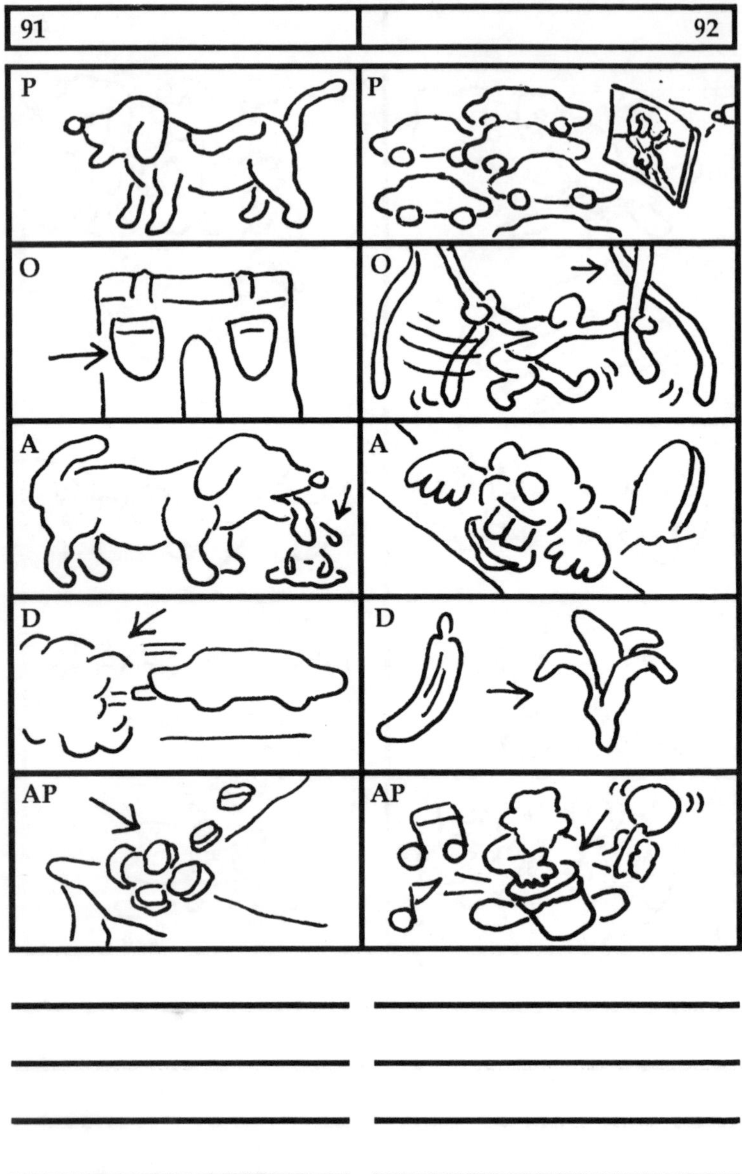

89. Parrot, Pants, Cluster, Vocal Cords,Concert
90. Parent, Hoe, Hijack, Starting Line, Tinsel

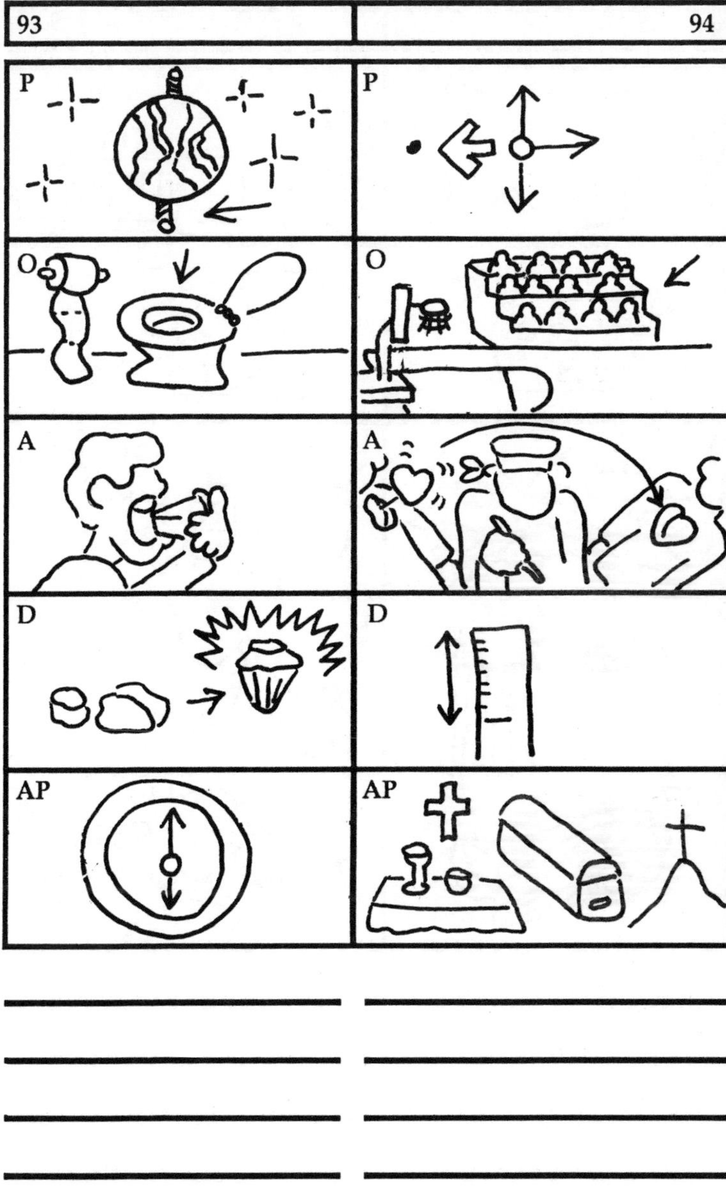

91, Dog, Pocket, Drool, Exhaust, Landslide
92. Drive-in, Vine, Gnaw, Banana Peel, Bongo Drums

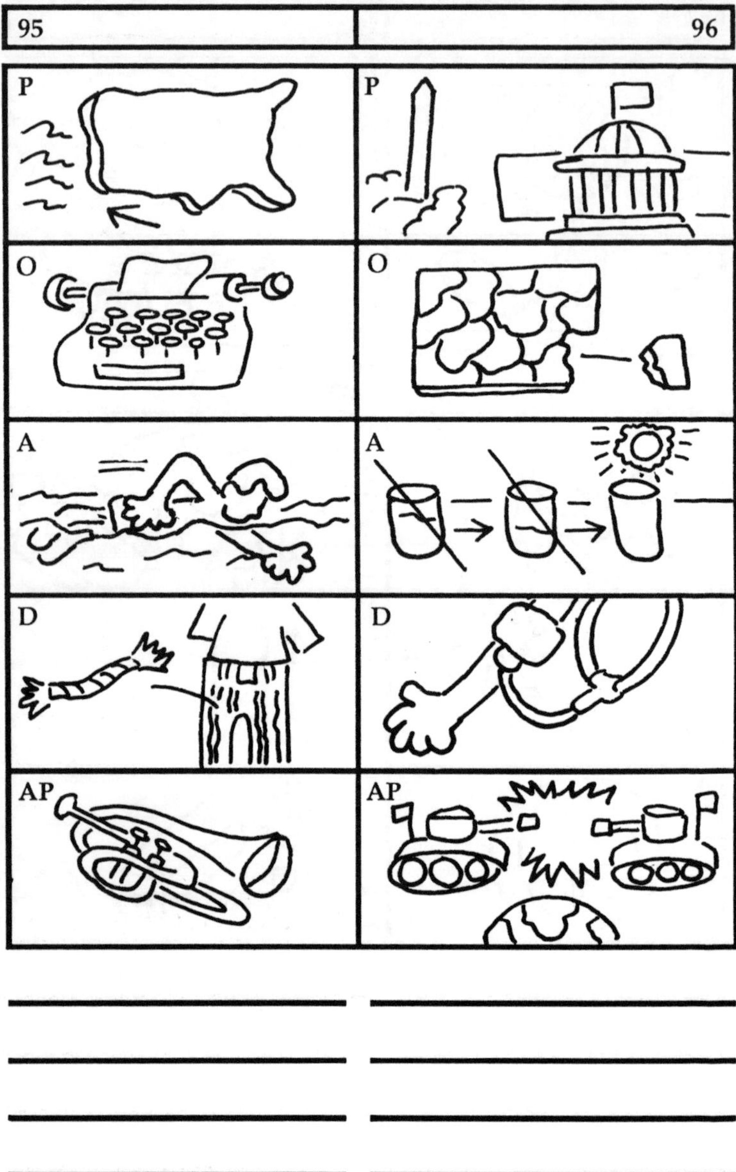

93. South Pole, Toilet, Eat, Gem, Six O'Clock
94. West, Bleacher, Transplant, Inch, Funeral

95. Pacific Ocean, Typewriter, Swim, Corduroy, Horn
96. Washington D.C., Puzzle, Evaporate, Blood Pressure, War

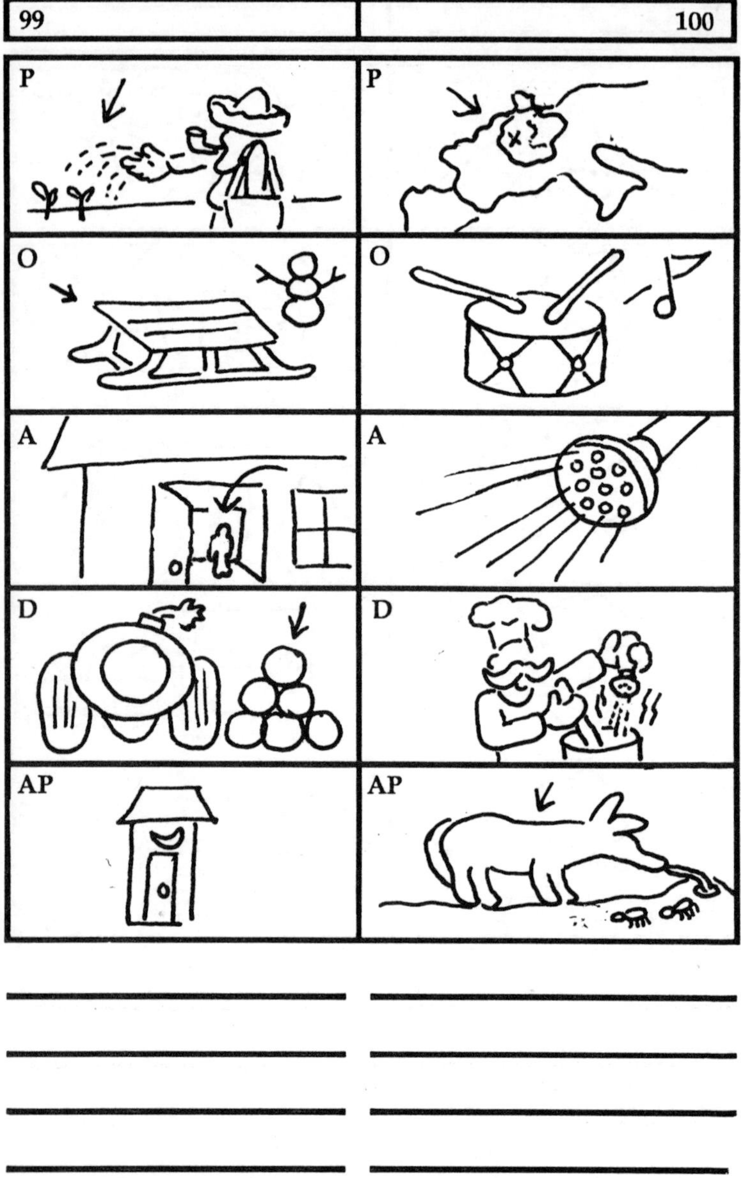

97. Roommate, Lighter, Surf, Mouth, Crew Neck
98. Toad, Pager, Ambush, Scrabble, Garage Sale

99. Sow, Sled, Enter, Cannonball, Outhouse
100. West Germany, Drum, Shower, Chef, Anteater

101. Switzerland, Balloon, Rise, Hayfever, Hyphen
102. Nebraska, Dead Bolt, Match, Stock Market, Organ Grinder

103. Stable, Inner Tube, Bleed, Baby Sitter, Insect
104. Penthouse, Chain Saw, Defeat, Knee Pads, Booth

105. Swordfish, Eyebrow Pencil, Pile, Pinky Ring, Hand Shake
106. Teeth, Streetcar, Golf, Steeple, War Paint

107. Granddaughter, Safety Net, Smash, Jug, Dud
108. Eyebrow, Smelling Salts, Toast, Fear, Rich

109. Matador, Album, Visit, Resort, Ten O'Clock
110. Peter Pan, Pill, Rob, Comedy, Art

111. Flamingo, Door, Burnt, Sandstorm, Yacht
112. Manicurist, Cactus, Perspire, Pepper, Tepee

113. Fox, Corkscrew, Interview, Front-Page, Spiked Heels
114. Officer, Ice Skate, Mature, Obstacle Course, Alcatraz

115. Termite, Lampshade, Throw, Disposal, Red Cross
116. Rhinoceros, Tent, Stretch, Temple, Robot

117. Fur, Balance Beam, Roast, Takeoff, Tear Gas
118. Leopard, Shrubs, Oppose, Bad, Forgery

119. Dentist, Jewelry, Top, Wastebasket, Toaster
120. California, Yolk, Bark, Year, Stairs

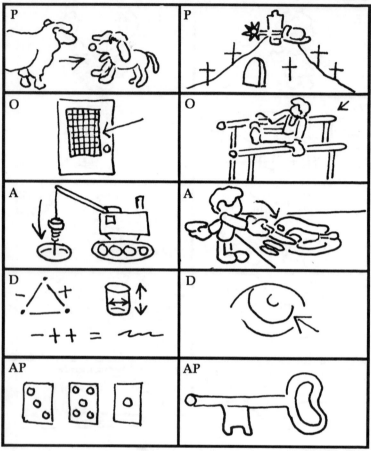

123	124

P	P
O	O
A	A
D	D
AP	AP

121. Bearded Lady, Piano, Drench, Foul Line, Smog
122. Lobster, Ornament, Rotate, Geography, Locomotive

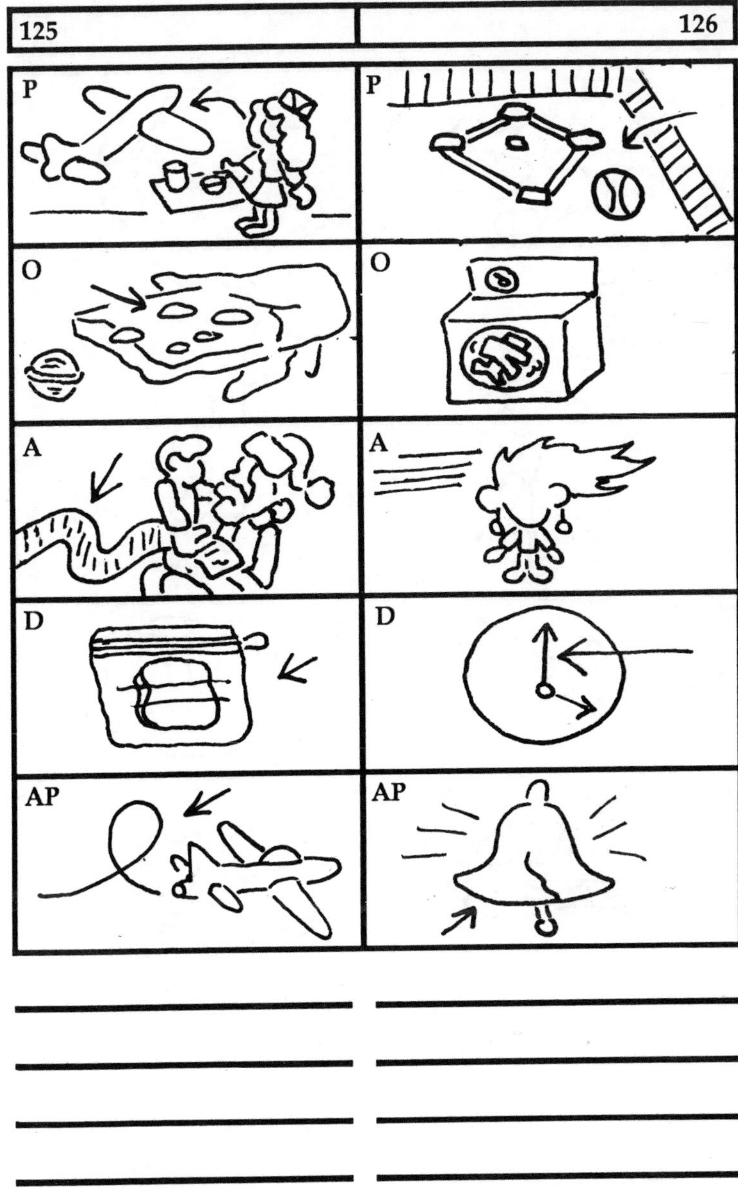

123. Sheepdog, Screen, Bore, Geometry, Odd
124. Boot Hill, Parallel Bars, Carve, Eyeball, Key

125. Stewardess, Almond, List, Plastic Bag, Loop
126. Ball Park, Dryer, Breeze, Big Hand, Liberty Bell

129	130
P	P
O	O
A	A
D	D
AP	AP

127. Infant, Footrest, Meet, Bucket Seat, Gale
128. Raccoon, Tree, Glow, Passport, Bunk Bed

129. Alligator, Garter Belt, Graze, Airstrip, Peace
130. Paddock, Shower Cap, Smoke, Sinuses, Fire Hydrant

131. Referee, Time Bomb, Rub, Barrier, Perpendicular
132. Lizard, Kayak, Boost, Phonograph, Steam Roller

133. Maid, Peg, Listen, Gondola, Field Goal
134. Convict, Nut, Scale, Smoke Screen, Permanent Press

135. Adam's Apple, Skateboard, Cork, Tea Kettle, Photo Finish
136. Lake, Stepladder, Rinse, Ivory, Tuxedo

137. Den, Leash, Detour, Dense, Rain Forest
138. Dictator, Chaise Longue, Bet, Red-Hot, Off

139. Paris, Mail, Pivot, Skillet, Picnic
140. Two Left Feet, Trash Compactor, Edge, Cheap, Hook

141. Duck, Pizza, Shave, Civil War, Blowpipe
142. Pagoda, Shag Carpet, Bandage, Diagram, Two

143. Town, Oilcan, Bat, None, Sunrise
144. Rancher, Gavel, Pry, Best, Belly Flop

145. Wolf, Container, Peck, Motorcade, Stick Shift
146. Ulcer, Thumbtack, Foam, Dagger, Headband

147. Earthworm, Drop, Claw, Amp, Big,
148. Florida, Tripod, Ricochet, Direction, Microphone

151	152
P	P
O	O
A	A
D	D
AP	AP

149. Jupiter, Hatchet, Untie, Poverty, Computer
150. Houston, Diaper, Frown, Half-Hour, Heel

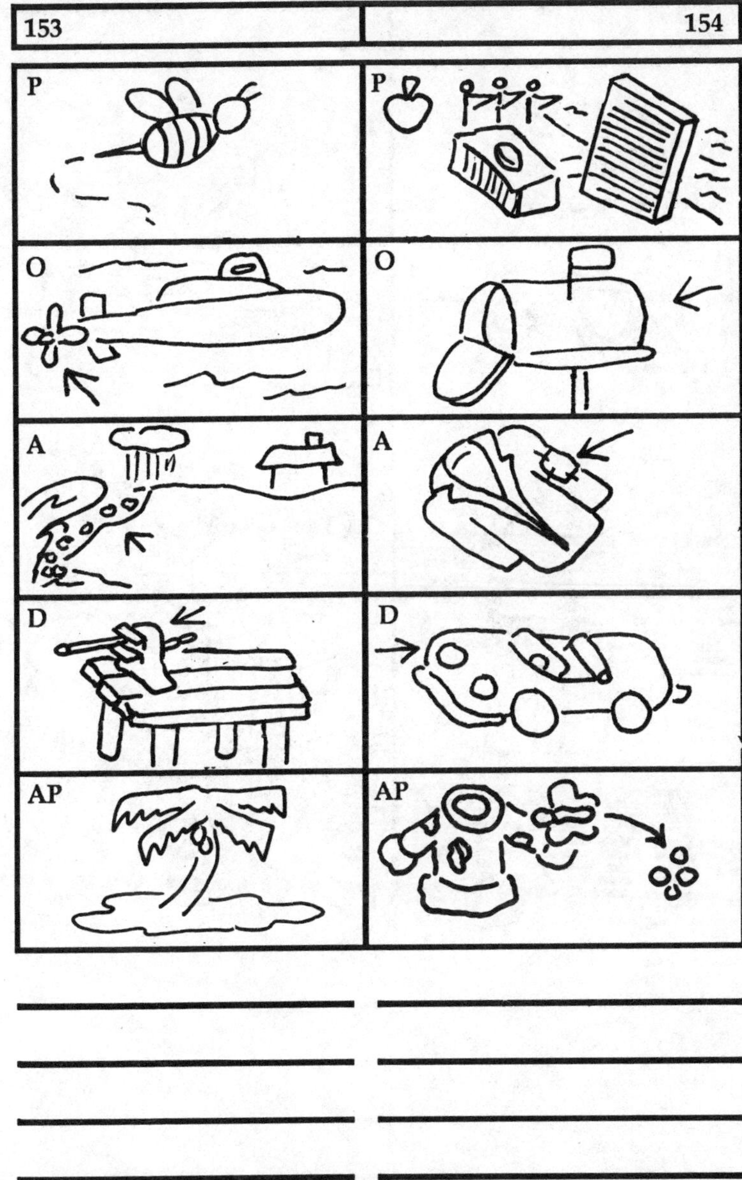

151. Starfish, Baggage, Tune, Hub Cap, Javelin
152. Skier, Poster, Yawn, Belly Dance, Deodorant

153. Bumblebee, Propeller, Erode, Vice, Palm
154. United Nations, Mailbox, Patch, Headlights, Mothball

155. College, Lens, Write, Denim, Blonde
156. Afro, Bus, Burst, Gazebo, Hard Hat

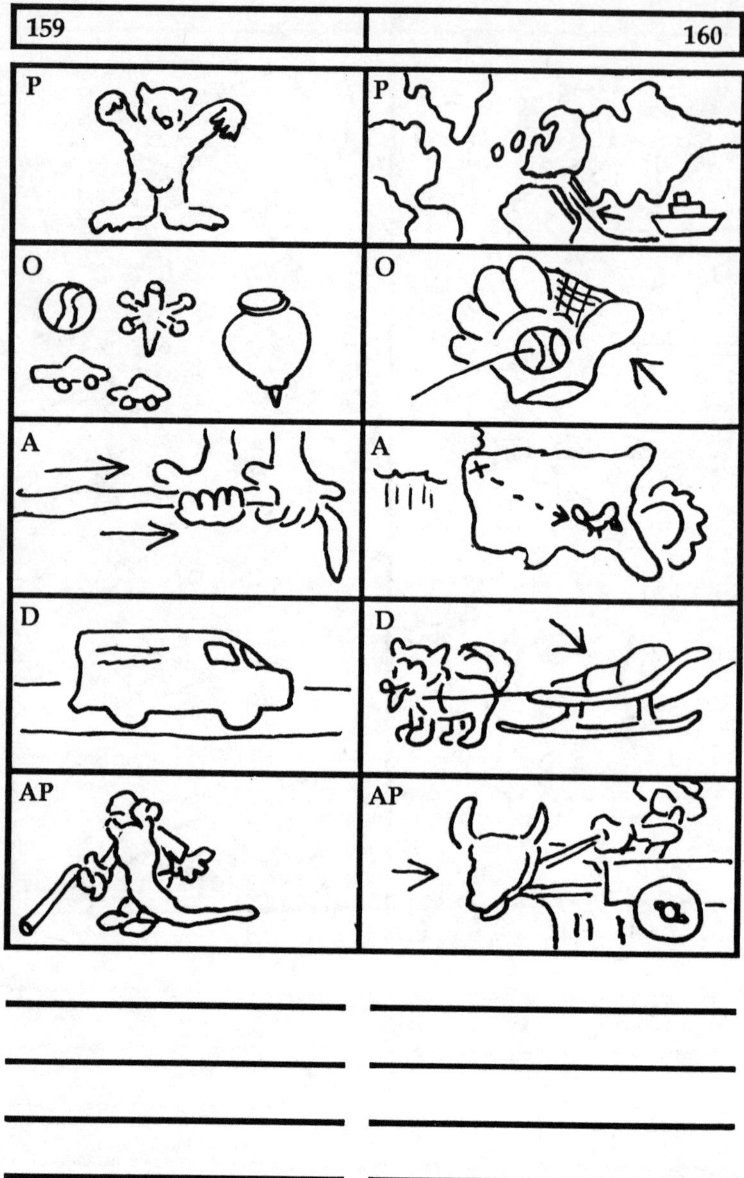

157. Doctor, Divot, Leak, Bonnett, Choir
158. Guard Dog, Seed, Tango, Infinity, Bent

159. Grizzly Bear, Toy, Pull, Van, Old
160. Suez Canal, Glove, Migrate, Dog Sled, Ox

161. Farmer, Pay Phone, Inject, Broken Leg, Dresser
162. Peacock, Strawberry, Fold, Penny, Trampoline

163. Subway, Hanger, Perk, Radiation, Bridge
164. Cupid, Snow Tire, Tiptoe, Soul, Cheek

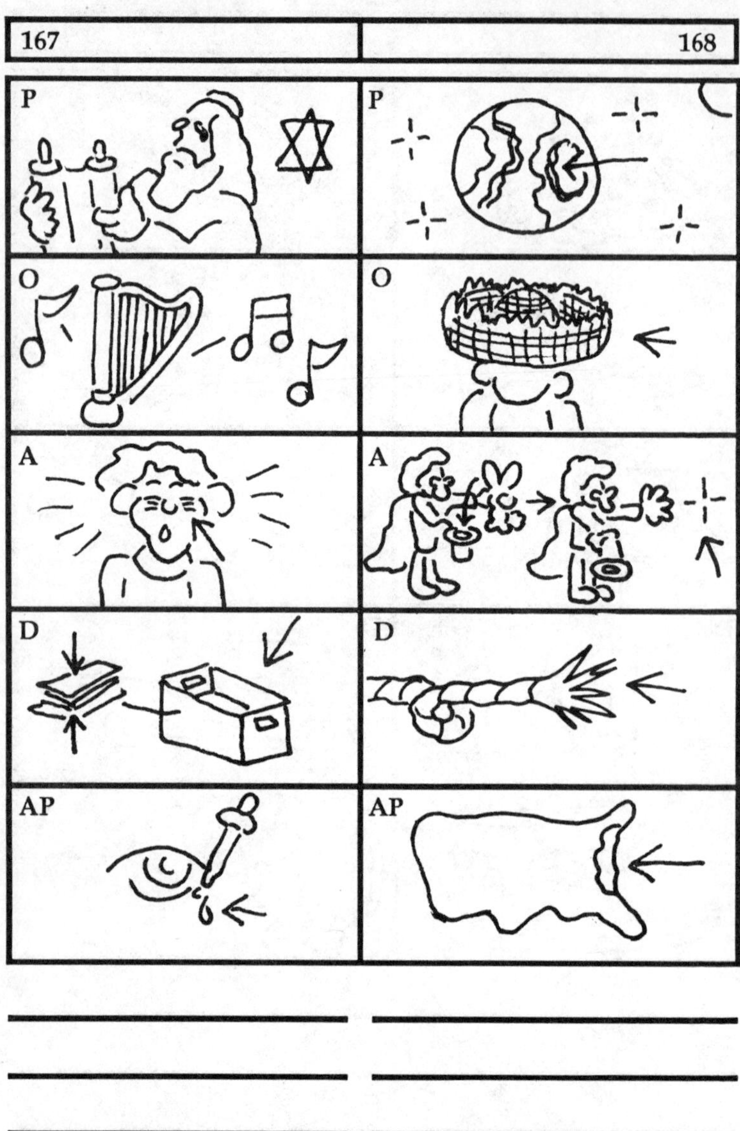

165. Overbite, Football, Defect, Crystal, Sking
166. Sardine, Vent, Recall, Cue Ball, Face-Lift

167. Rabbi, Harp, Blush, Cardboard Box, Eye Drops
168. Continent, Straw Hat, Disappear, End, East Coast

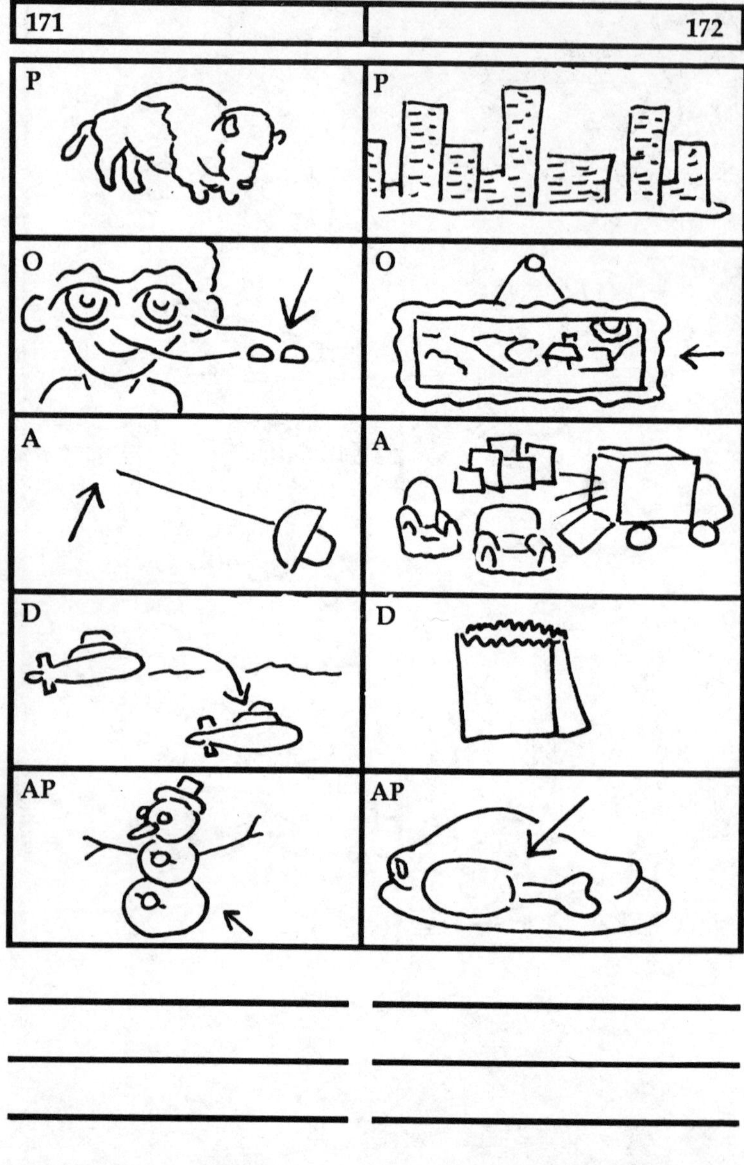

169. Forearm, Toothpick, Pad, Soundproof, Conveyor
170. Maine, Scissors, Putt, Rod, Curb

171. Buffalo, Contact Lens, Tip, Submerge, Snowman
172. City, Picture, Move, Paper Sack, Drumstick

173. Soviet Union, Coaster, Poke, Imprint, Whirlpool
174. House, Fountain, Echo, Digital Watch, Pebble

175. Mechanic, Rifle, Tilt, Butter, Brim
176. Stepfather, Overcoat, Jab, Blackout, Roof

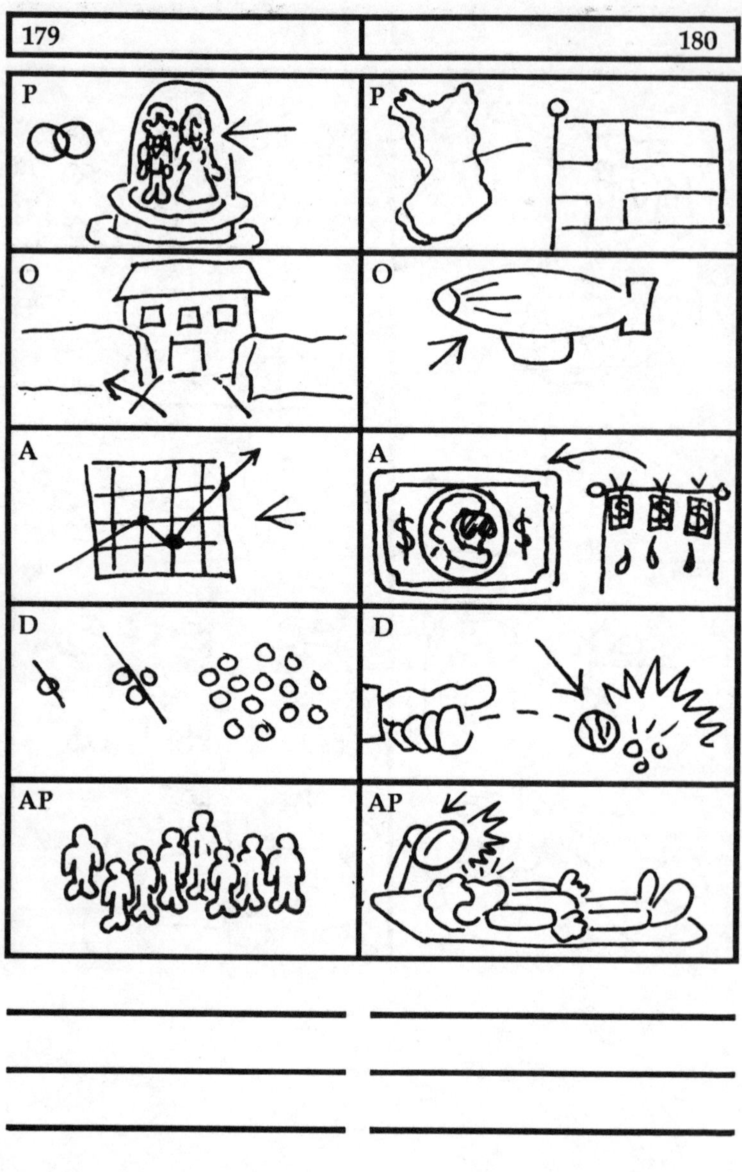

177. Giraffe, Wheel, Turn, Yes, Sky
178. Father, Couch, Paddle, Profit, Water

179. Bride, Hedge, Graph, Many, People
180. Finland, Blimp, Counterfeit, Marble, Sun Lamp

181. Museum, Slat, Tow, Mohawk, Rim
182. Knuckle, Snowmobile, Bomb, Funny Papers, Pin Stripe

183. Crab, Hammock, Mine, Smoke Ring, Midair
184. Jaguar, Easel, Call, Mush, River

185. Pilot, Nozzle, Hitchhike, Sweatbox, Small
186. Missing Link, Blouse, Heat, Crescent, Left

187. Miner, Stone, Wad, Extension Cord, Hip
188. Playboy, Boat, Steer, Polka Dot, Earphone

189. Egypt, Paper Clip, Knit, Novel, Bird Bath
190. Lap, Fishing Pole, Glance, Language, Pipe

191. Dad, Book, Bruise, Kosher, Totem Pole
192. Body, Sofa, Reject, Shaft, Glob

195	196

193. Great Britain, Tumble Weed, Lynch, Centerpiece, Little
194. Fire Station, Banana, Reverse, Volleyball, Around

195. Canada, Nail File, Hem, Asteroid, Pot
196. Funny Bone, Waterbed, Mix, Drift, Chalk

197, Amazon River, Emery Board, Hug, Pinky, Pirate
198. False Teeth, Cube, Torpedo, Fragrance, Posse

199. Double Chin, Color T.V., Model, Mural, Neighborhood
200. Beard, Candy Cane, Laugh, String, Ear

201. Grand Canyon, Jar, Miss, Jumper Cable, Place Mat
202. Playroom, Boots, Roll, Shoulder Strap, Charades

203. Israel, Watermelon, Compute, Phantom, Mind
204. Cemetery, Jet, Shampoo, Drowsy, Mud

205. Illinois, Biscuit, Choke, Matchbook, Cousin
206. Bomb Shelter, Helicopter, Clink, Rabies, Freeway

207. Ant, Pumpkin, Erase, Warehouse, Big Dipper
208. White House, Swing, Boil, Mile, Jump Rope

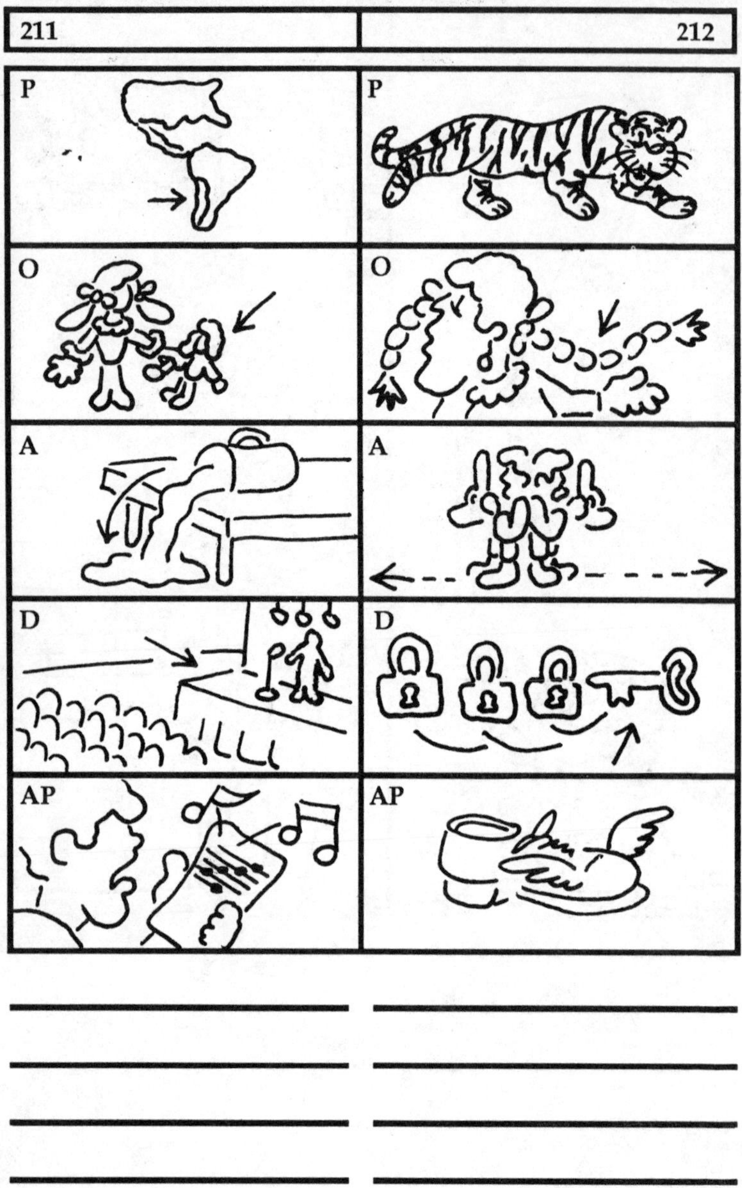

209. Tooth, Sling, Launch, Spatula, Train
210. Ranch, Lapel, Curl, Foreign, Doorstop

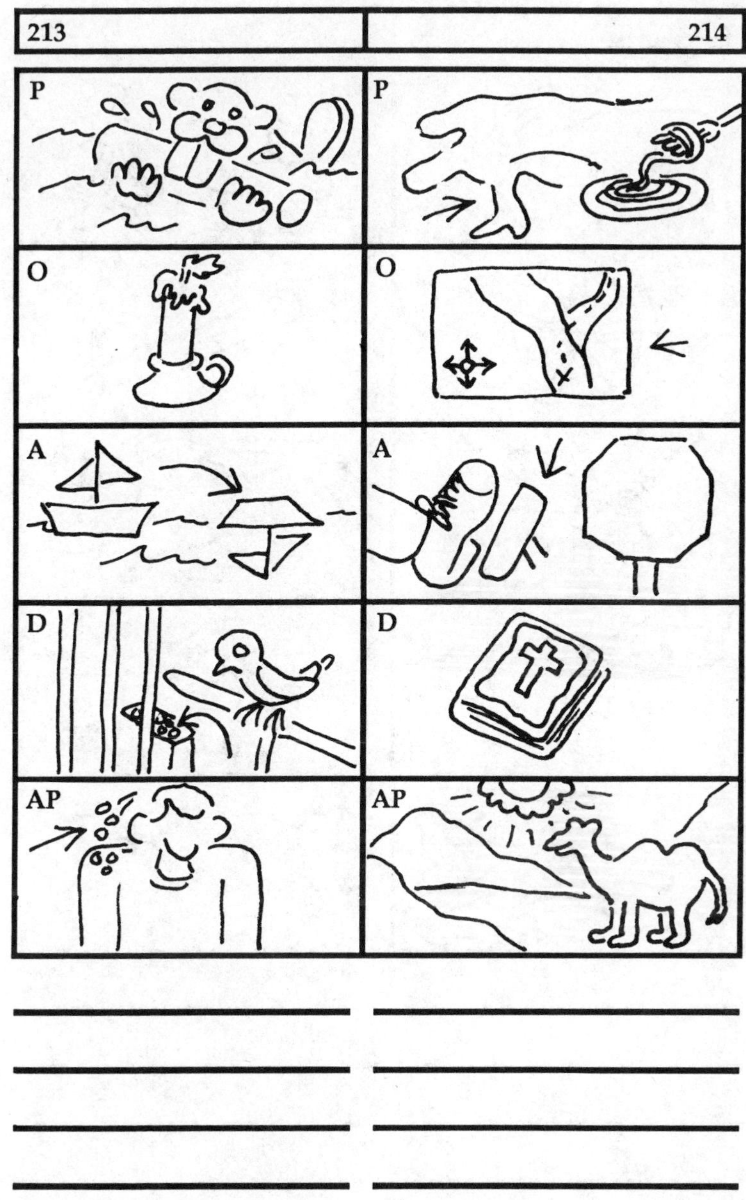

211. Chile, Doll, Spill, Stage, Song
212. Tiger, Braid, Duel, Master Key, Wing-Tips

213. Beaver, Candle, Capsize, Bird Seed, Dandruff
214. Italy, Map, Brake, Bible, Sahara Desert

215. Goat, Spokes, Wet, Nose Plugs, Dragon
216. France, Pencil, Gallop, Ferris Wheel, Stake

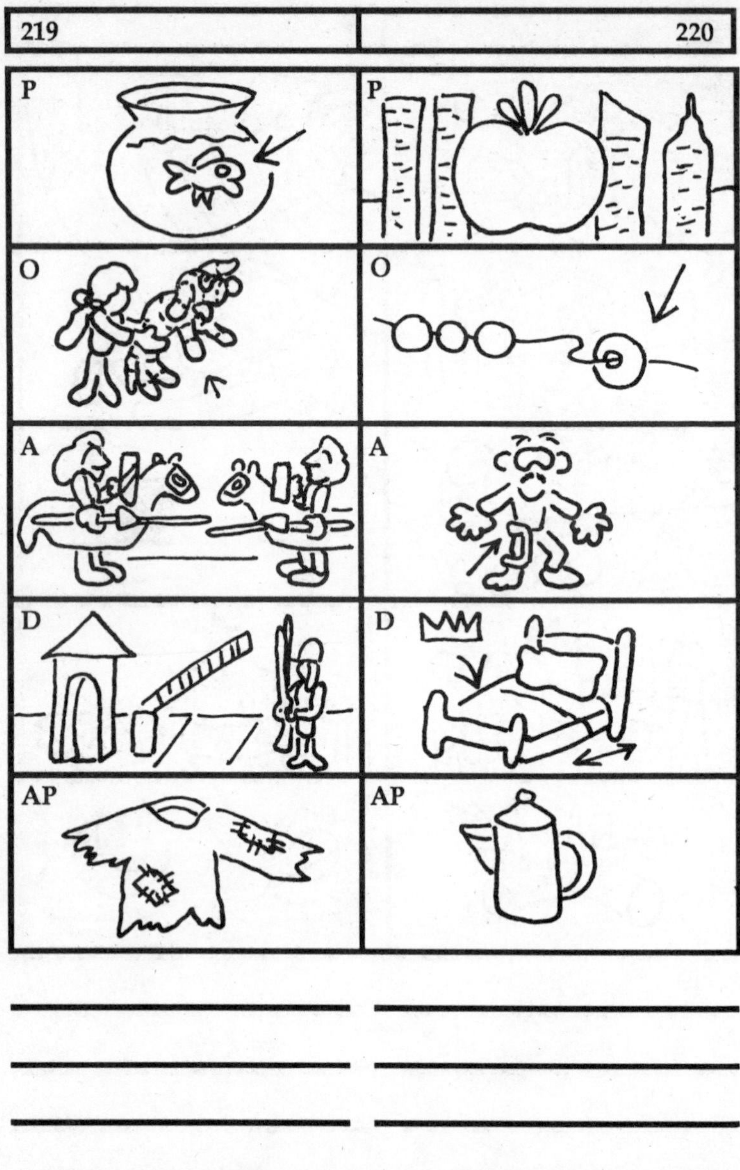

217. Grandfather, Spoon, Wag, Single File, Fire
218. Galaxy, Mattress, Black, Christmas, Night

219. Goldfish, Stuffed Animal, Joust, Border Line, Ragged
220. New York, Bead, Brace, Kingsize Bed, Coffeepot

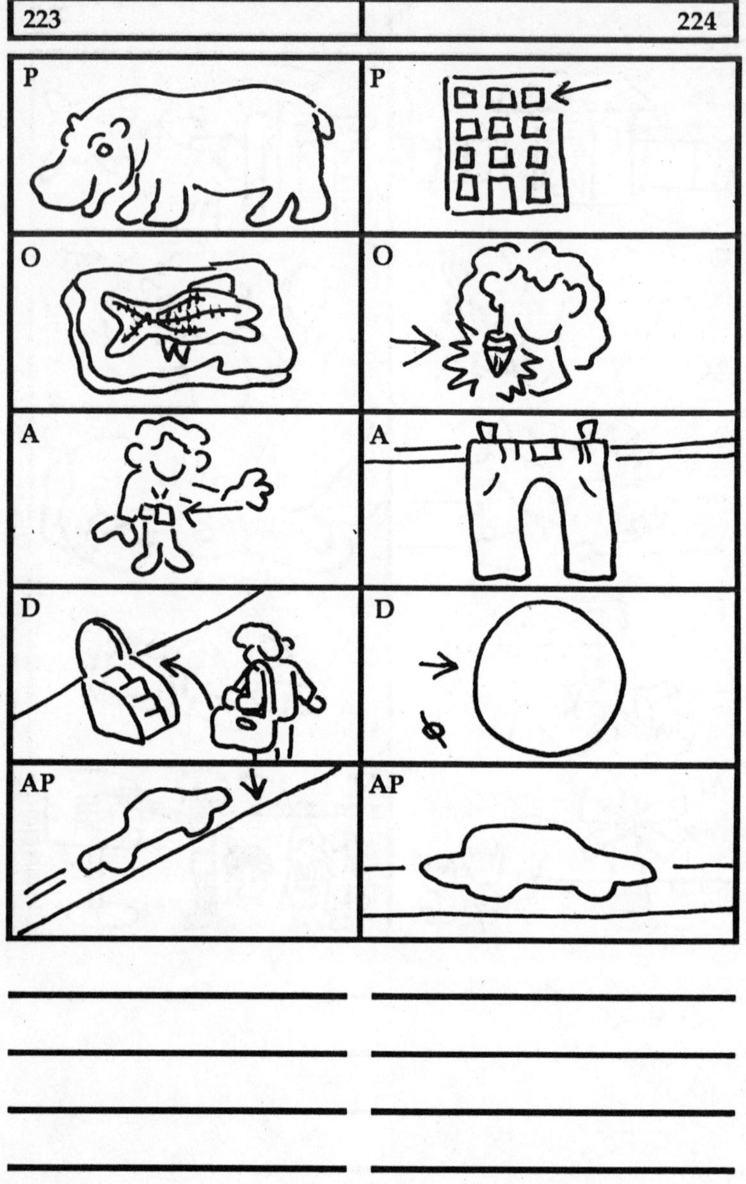

221. Shed, Pogo Stick, Crash-Land, Look, Windmill
222. Los Angeles, Toupee, Stub, Capsule, Wilt Chamberlain

223. Hippopotamus, Fossil, Buckle, Carry-On, Steep
224. Office, Diamond Earring, Pant, Huge, Car

225. Hornet, Swiss Cheese, Sweat, Appliance, Drive
226. Brazil, Onion, Shrink, Arena, Marshmallow

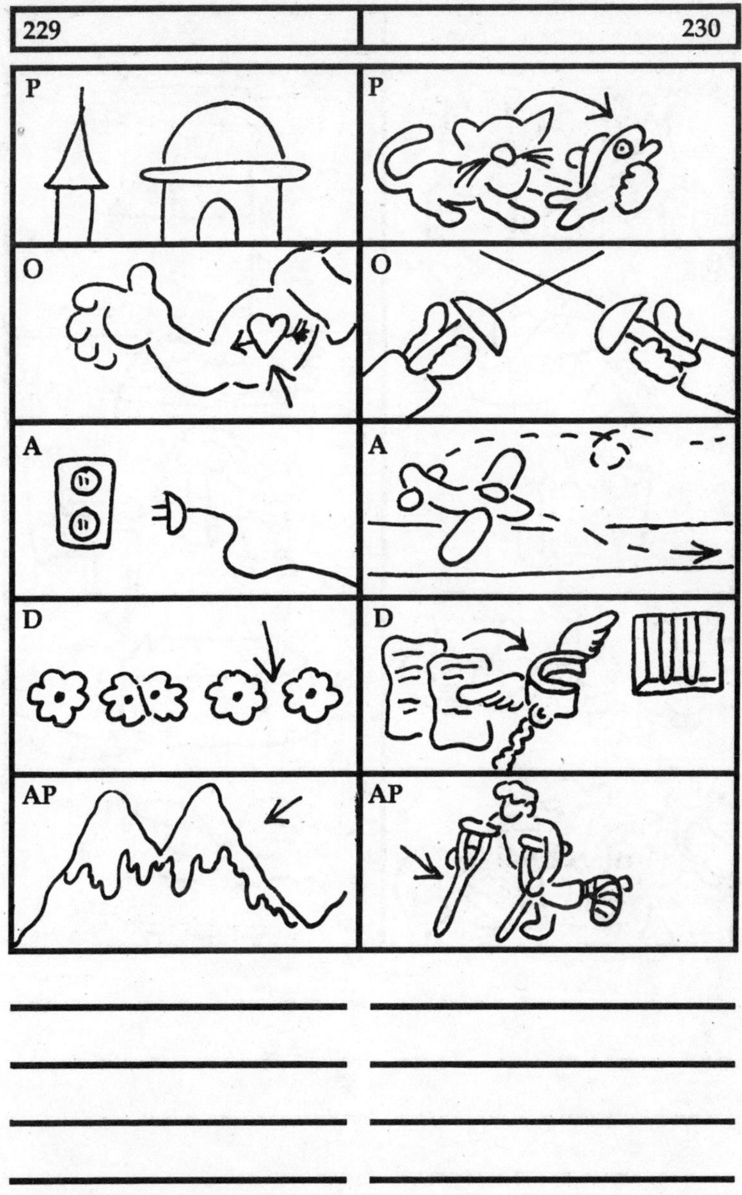

227. Singer, Shawl, Tread, Two-By-Four, Dice
228. United States, Dart, Pave, Muff, Prison

229. Mosque, Tattoo, Plug, Separation, Glacier
230. Catfish, Fence, Approach, Parole, Crutches

231. Prince, Picnic Basket, Bag, Unanimous, Pony Express
232. Home, Mat, Sit, Back Door, Heaven

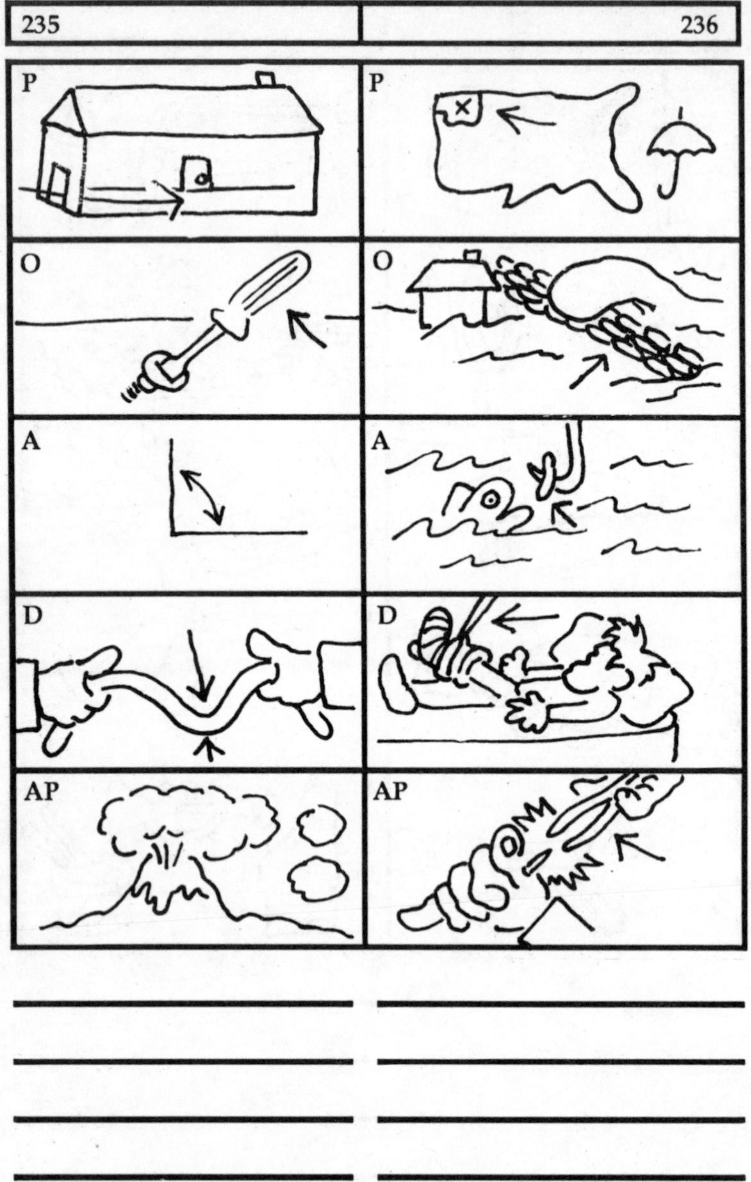

233. **Skull, Target, File, Prescription, Cartwheel**
234. **Bus Station, Statue, Dream, Convex, Instrument**

235. Hall, Screwdriver, Angle, Slack, Volcano
236. Seattle, Sandbag, Bait, Traction, Tweezers

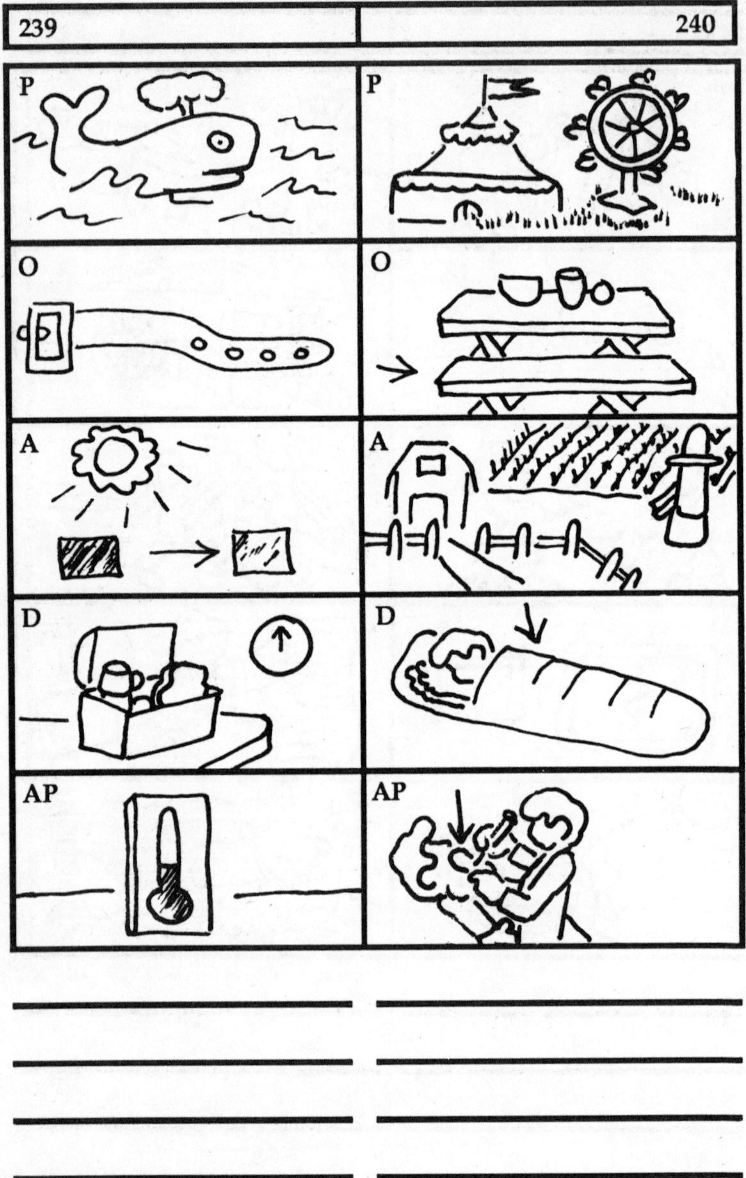

237. Horse, Hose, Chisel, Inflation, Shadow
238. Stadium, Ivy, March, Sermon, Flipper

239. Whale, Belt, Fade, Lunch, Thermometer
240. Carnival, Bench, Farm, Sleeping Bag, Numb

241. Robin, Fly Swatter, Blond, Colon, Stripe
242. Fin, Bicycle, Brew, Speed Limit, Deep

243. President, Top Hat, Spray, Bridle, Eiffel Tower
244. Puppy, Bikini, Somersault, Loud, Nuclear

245. Bee, Lace, Ride, Banner, Crew Cut
246. Tusk, Carnation, Soar, Lift-Off, Curve

247. Barn, Kite, Chop, Slide Rule, Attic
248. Tarantula, Pretzel, Follow, Sun Screen, Person

249. Muscle, Footlocker, Paste, Space Walk, Illusion
250. Carpenter, Reclining Chair, Dry, Billion, Hairspray

251. Tongue, Banjo, Prick, For Sale, Old Faithful
252. Utah, Axle, Pollute, Padding, Cordless

253. Dump, Robe, Rut, Towel Rack, Northern Lights
254. World, Shaver, Measure, Sleep Walk, Cross-Legged

255. Taiwan, Skirt, Cry, Lake Front, Short
256. Reindeer, Strap, Ram, Diameter, Remote Control

257. Foot, Jack-In-The-Box, Voice, Beer Bottle, Snow Storm
258. Pharaoh, Steak, Snore, Sit-Up, Ski Run

259. Vancouver, Ribbon, Quack, Indoor, Knee
260. Heart, Speaker, Intercept, Cross Fire, Pyramid

261. Moustache, Radio, Divide, Little Hand, Cocoon
262. Slug, Credit Card, Soak, Marathon, Bald

263. Ladybug, Boomerang, Glare, Runny Nose, Towel
264. Alaska, Stoplight, Ferry, Homesick, Floor

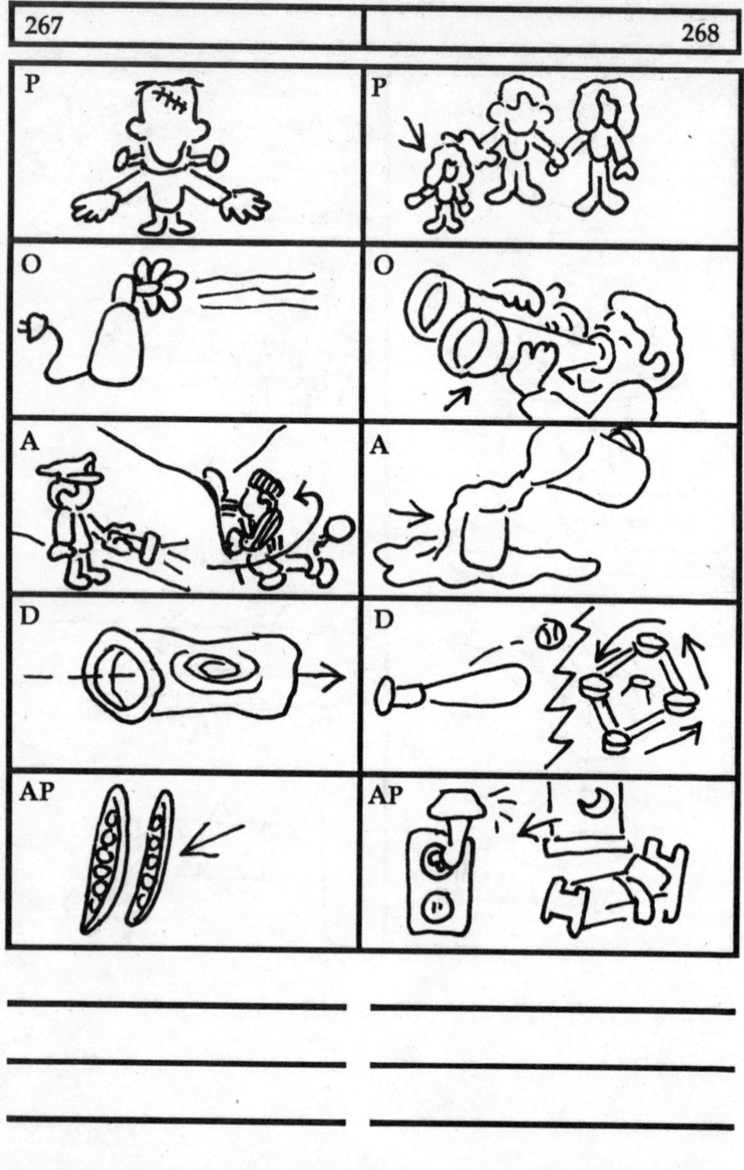

265. Tummy, Skates, Massage, Shoe Box, Mushroom
266. Porpoise, Decoy, Rake, Ballast, Religion

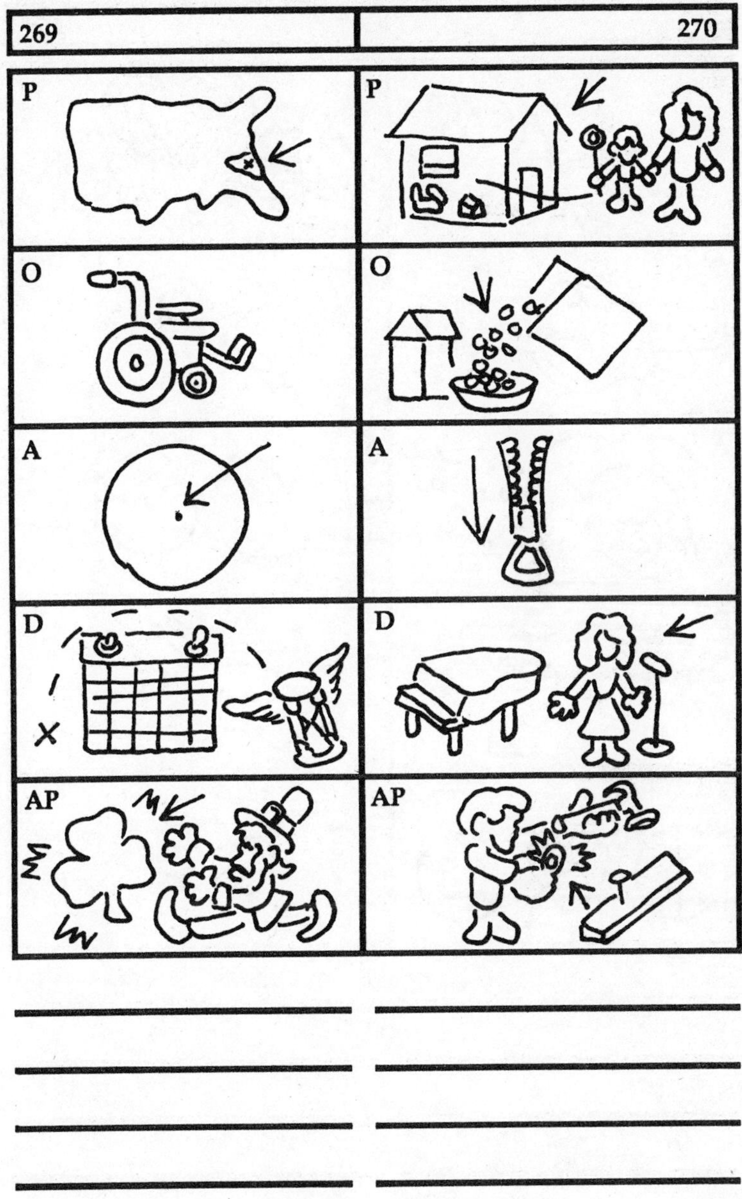

267. Monster, Fan, Evade, Hollow, String Bean
268. Daughter, Binoculars, Overflow, Triple, Night Light

269. South Carolina, Wheelchair, Center, Leap Year, Shamrock
270. Kindergarten, Cereal, Unzip, Solo, Pain

271. Mount Everest, Watch Band, Hibernate, Emerald, Joy
272. Camp, Cane, Fight, Ski Rack, Face

273. Sailor, Reflector, Pole-Vault, Unconscious, Jungle
274. Bridesmaid, Pacemaker, Deport, Card Table, Sad

275. Athlete, Flame Thrower, Muzzle, Mad, Champagne
276. Walrus, Paper Doll, Hiccup, Alfalfa, Chandelier

277. Father-In-Law, Dustpan, Sting, Cotton Candy, Grandchild
278. Soldier, Needle, Survey, Festival, Cassette

279. Jail, Knob, Cap, Red Wine, Postcard
280. Beatnik, Mud Flap, Brush, Dunce Cap, Feet

281. Tijuana, Tube, Pitch, Scramble, Cave
282. Georgia, Sword, Perch, Gray, Cyclops

283. Rabbit, Soup Spoon, Dam, Pantsuit, Mummy
284. Elbow, Tailgate, Skydive, Dance, Lid

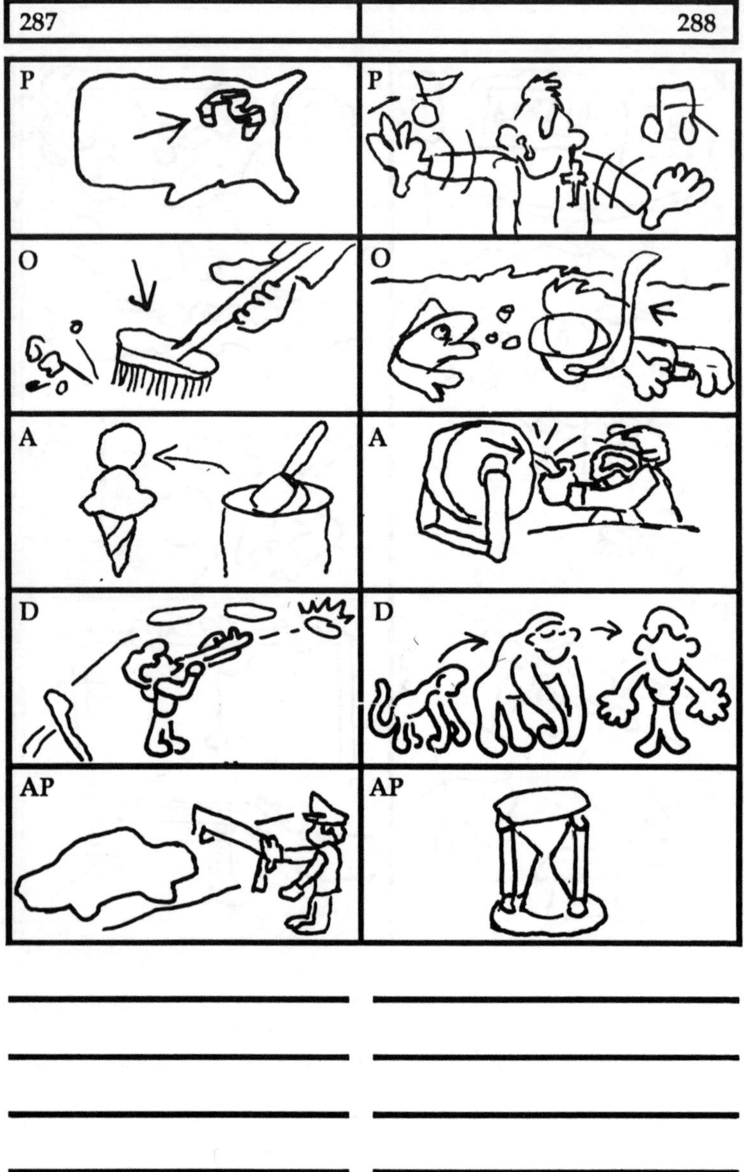

285. Art Gallery, Raindrop, Dangle, Handwriting, Lightning Rod
286. Rodeo, Tugboat, Daydream, Chin-Up, Machine Gun

287. Great Lakes, Broom, Scoop, Skeet, Roadblock
288. Punk Rocker, Snorkel, Grind, Evolution, Hourglass

289. Shopping Center, Reel, Knock, Cordless, Shirley Temple
290. Church, Apron, Strike, Wild, Waterproof

291, Solar System, Safe, Wink, Whole, Handsome
292. Sweden, Motorcycle, Conquer, Blubber, Hand

293. Bald Eagle, Sail, Rage, Record, Valley
294. Clown, Mistletoe, Raise, Warm, Leapfrog

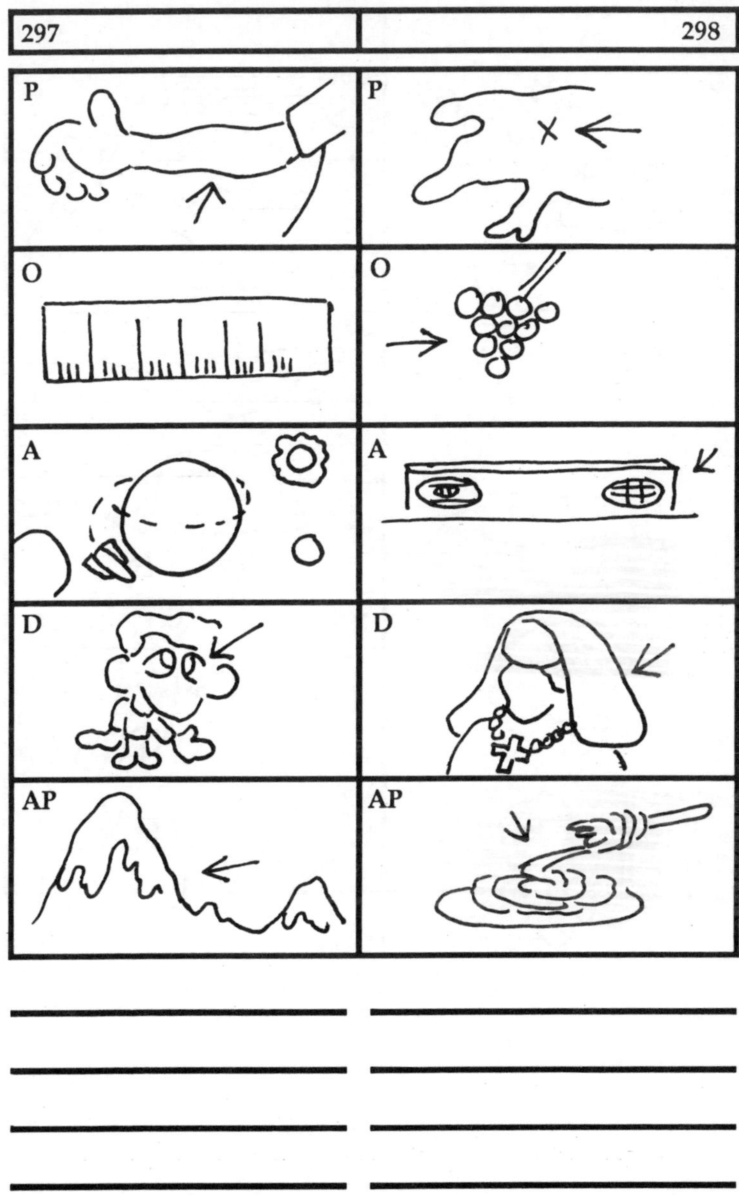

295. Greenland, Wheelbarrow, Free, Musk, Bucket
296. Vampire, Veil, Rain, Gallery, Greenhouse

297. Arm, Ruler, Orbit, Cross-Eyed, Mountain
298. Germany, Grape, Level, Habit, Noodle

299. Frog, Silo, Plot, Cauliflower, Reflection
300. Mt. St. Helens, Anchor, Iron, Giftwrap, Rectangle

301. Middle East, Cracker, Trip, Health, Stump
302. Shark, Abacus, Toss, Cauldron, Submarine

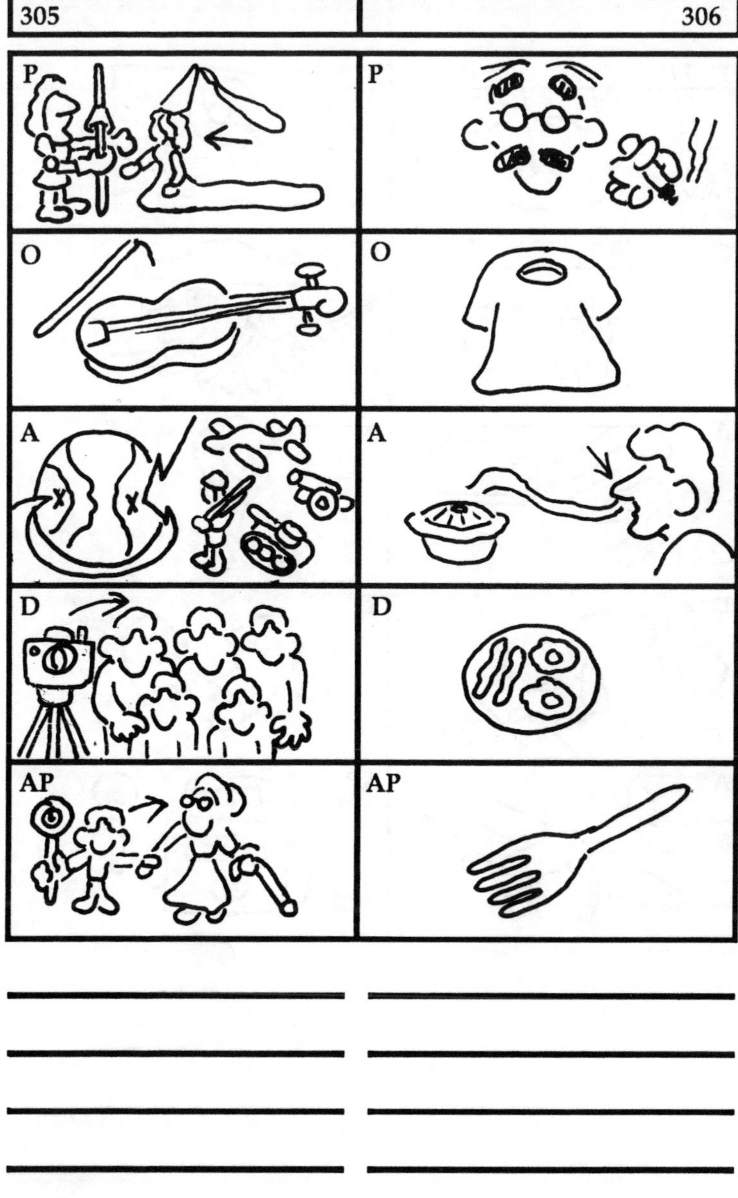

303. Shetland Pony, Shoe, Cue, Lurch, Air
304. Sister, Igloo, Bite, Elastic, Wagon Train

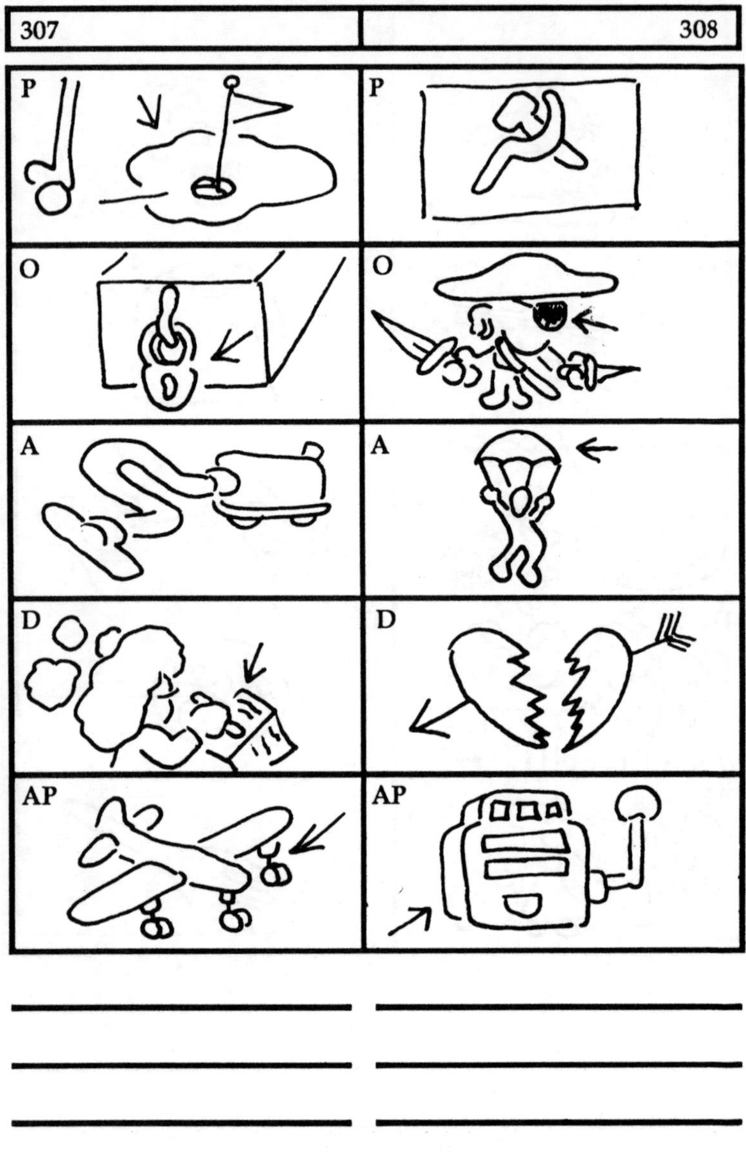

305. Lady, Violin, Invade, Group, Grandmother
306. Groucho Marx, T-Shirt, Smell, Bacon and Eggs, Fork

309	310

P	P
O	O
A	A
D	D
AP	AP

307. Putting Green, Padlock, Vacuum, Diary, Landing Gear
308. Russia, Eye Patch, Parachute, Broken Heart, Slot Machine

309. Squid, Laser Beam, Weed, Multiply, Surfing
310. Killer Whale, Napkin, Huddle, Reflect, Dark

311. Rome, Chair, Stop, Pop, Overcast
312. Big Apple, Flight Bag, Stuff, Travelers' Check, Goatee

313. **Brain, Waffle, Love, Recline, Beach Ball**
314. **Squirrel, Card, Parade, Plastic, Teardrop**

315. Venus, Pinwheel, Pose, Laundry, Wagon Wheel
316. India, Nail Polish, Howl, Trench, Cannon

317. Montana, Miniskirt, Hit, Lawn Bowling, Navel
318. Little Dipper, Welcome Mat, Lure, Bermuda Shorts, Goose Bumps

321	322

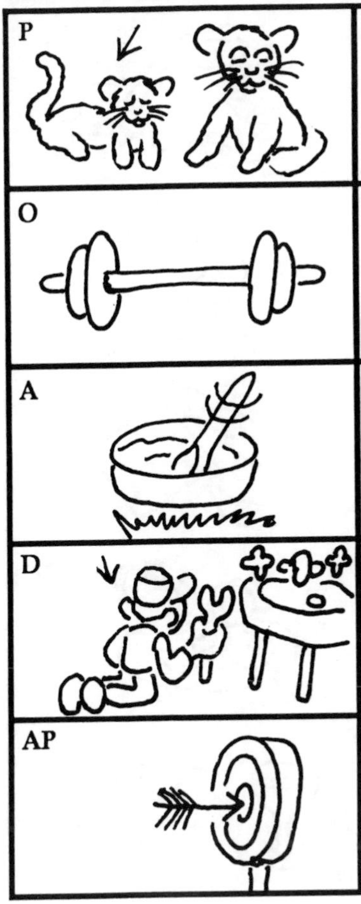

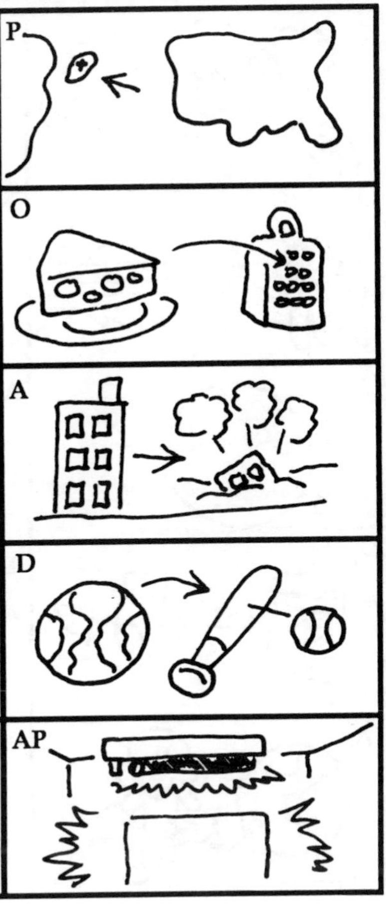

P	P
O	O
A	A
D	D
AP	AP

319. Skeleton, Gong, Fingerprint, Drought, Black Eye
320. Pilgrim, Fly Paper, Walk, Eclipse, Chopsticks

321. Kitten, Barbell, Stir, Repairman, Bull's-Eye
322. Tokyo, Cheese Grater, Raze, World Series, Black Light

323. Cheerleader, Noah's Ark, Spot, Music, Poor
324. Molar, Alarm Clock, Pour, Meatball, Wine Glass

325. Saint Bernard, Shield, Make, Poem, Rattle
326. Patio, Carrot, Quote, Paddy Wagon, Pearl Necklace

327. Doghouse, Gate, Tear, Flask, Round
328. Downstairs, Crowbar, Fracture, Average, Bow Tie

331	332

329. Finger, Bowl, Point, Dove, Convoy
330. Caterpillar, Box, Yodel, Sapphire, Victory

331. Bigfoot, X-Ray, Divorce, Newsstand, Nostril
332. Donkey, Unicycle, Cook, Mule, Pole

333. Moscow, Pennant, Drape, Willow, Jury
334. Stream, Baseball, Ask, Windy, Titanic

337	338
P	P
O	O
A	A
D	D
AP	AP

335. Witch Doctor, Buoy, Wrap, Curly Hair, Braille
336. Stork, Clover, Lift, Party, Lighthouse

337. Cheetah, Sheet, Spread, Defense, Percent
338. Cat, Dime, Attack, Unhappy, Spaceship

341	342

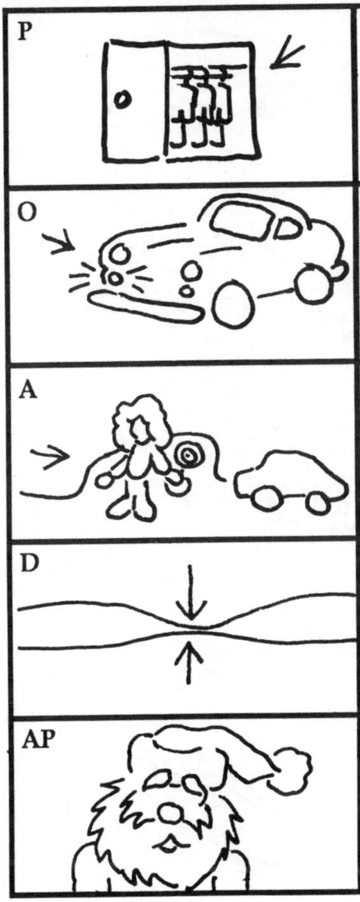

P	P
O	O
A	A
D	D
AP	AP

339. Shoulder, Seat Belt, Stare, Plaque, Castle
340. Mouth, Gangplank, Hunch, Quiet, Cutoffs

341. Closet, Blinker, Avoid, Narrow, Santa Claus
342. Swamp, Cross, Control, Ledge, Trunk

345	346
P	P
O	O
A	A
D	D
AP	AP

343. Octopus, Petal, Hear, Pore, Fondue
344. New Orleans, Popcorn, Pump, Barnacle, Cork

345. Cleopatra, Umbrella, Bind, Tiny, Revolving Door
346. Madrid, Crown, Mutiny, Strength, Life Preserver

347. Country, Hamburger, Swallow, Death Valley, Laryngitis
348. Living Room, Cookie, Scar, Locket, Ribs

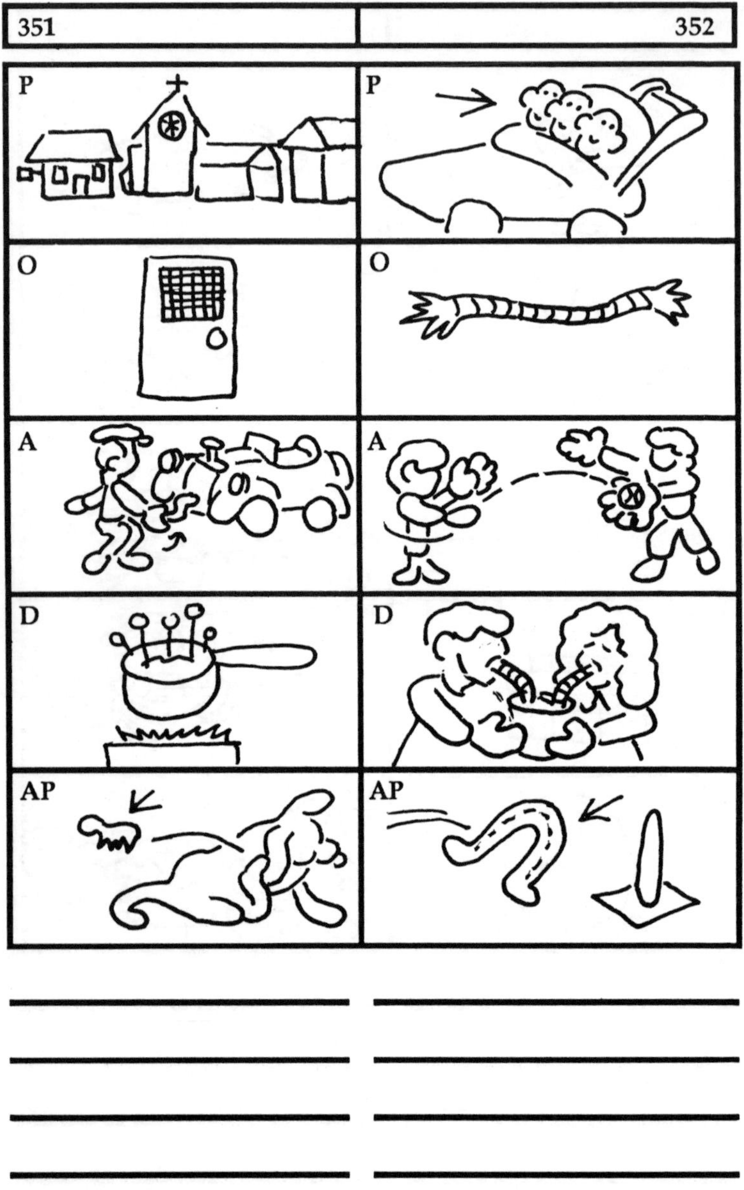

349. Boy Scout, Mannequin, Rock, Monday, Second Hand
350. Pig, Brass Knuckles, Win, Cheshire Cat, Diaper Rash

351. Village, Screen Door, Crank, Boiling Water, Flea
352. Triplets, Rope, Lob, Share, Horseshoe

353. Underground, Suspenders, Muffle, Lumberjack, Blind
354. Crocodile, Skis, Mug, Beehive, Searchlight

355. London, Crystal Ball, Note, Crumb, Wedding
356. Litterbug, Tape, Merge, Water Polo, Cowcatcher

357. Thumb, Bullet, Repeat, Telephone Book, Son
358. Snake, Window, Check, Spot, Rocket

359. Mona Lisa, Surfboard, Test, Spark Plug, Money
360. Polar Bear, Cup, Harpoon, Plump, Cabin

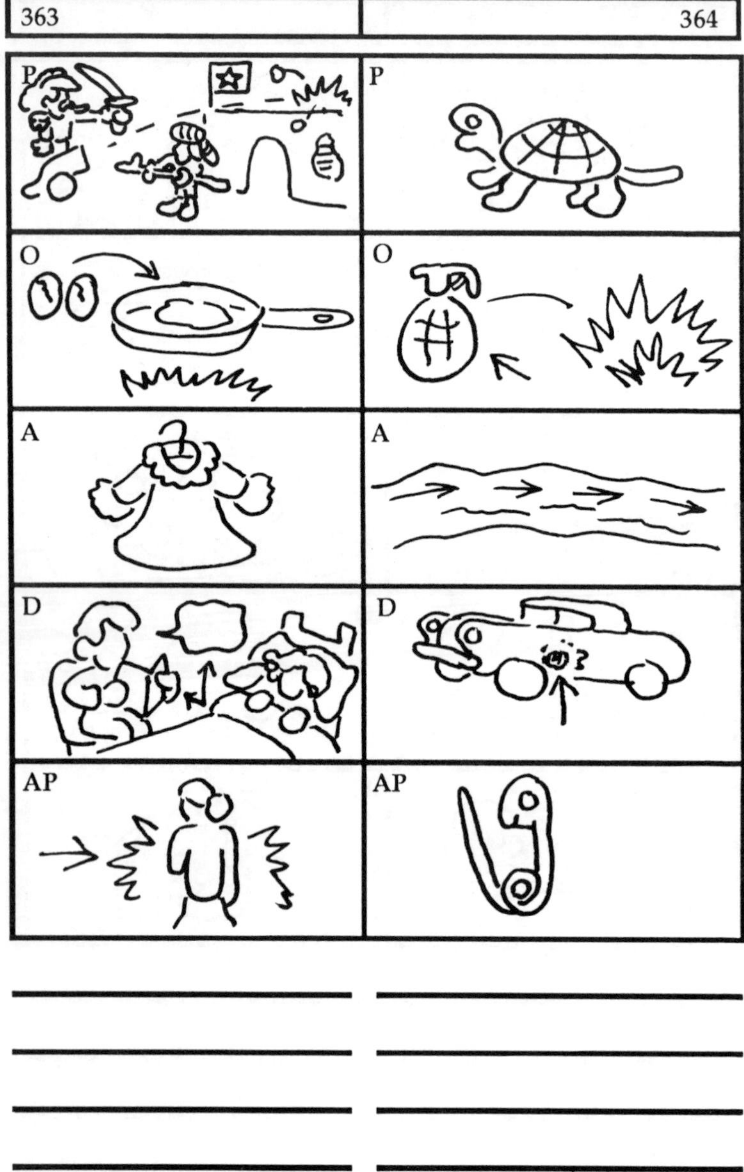

361. Monkey, Christmas Tree, Manicure, Firing Squad, Contagious
362. Cow, Handlebar, Swarm, Radial Tire, Candlelight

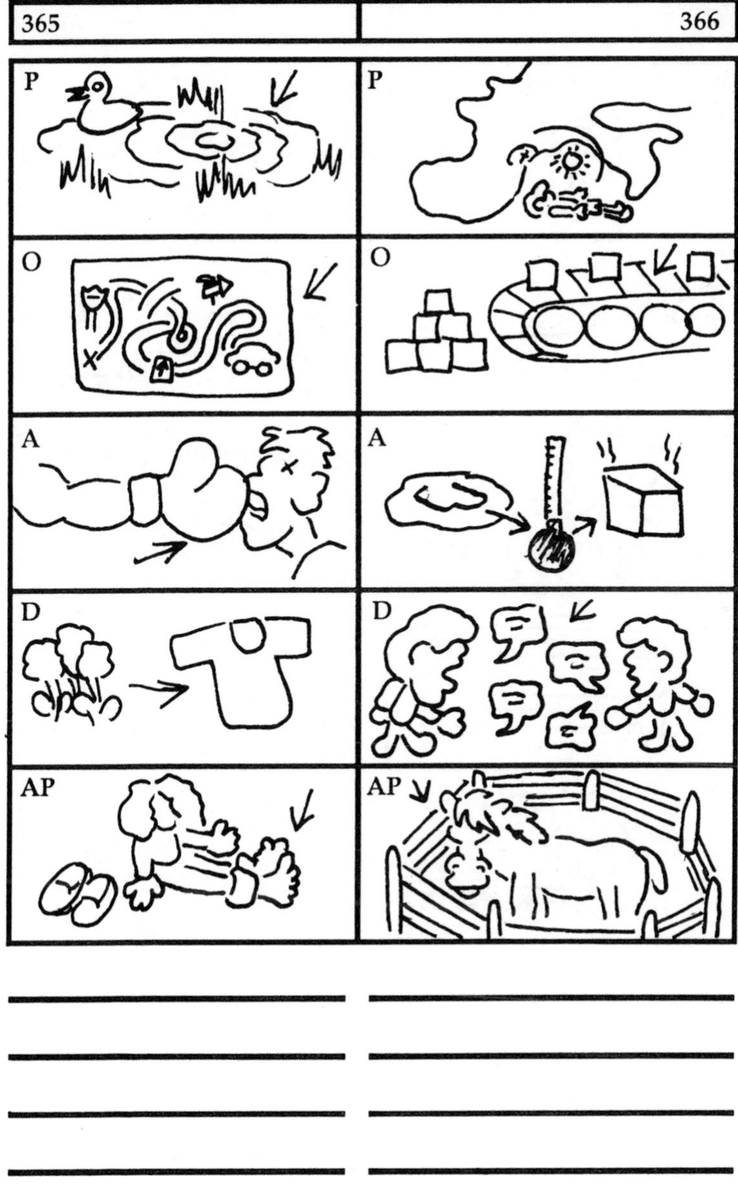

363, Alamo, Omelet, Dress, Story, Venus De Milo
364. Turtle, Grenade, Flow, Rust, Safety Pin

365. Pond, Road Map, Punch, Cotton, Barefoot
366. Riviera, Conveyor Belt, Freeze, Conversation, Corral

367. Stepdaughter, Copier, Pinch, Amtrak, Stomach Ache
368. Boulevard, Furniture, View, House Call, Woman

369. Ronald Reagan, Candelabra, Shiver, Croissant, Mars
370. Praying Mantis, Spotlight, Pin, Sprint, Where

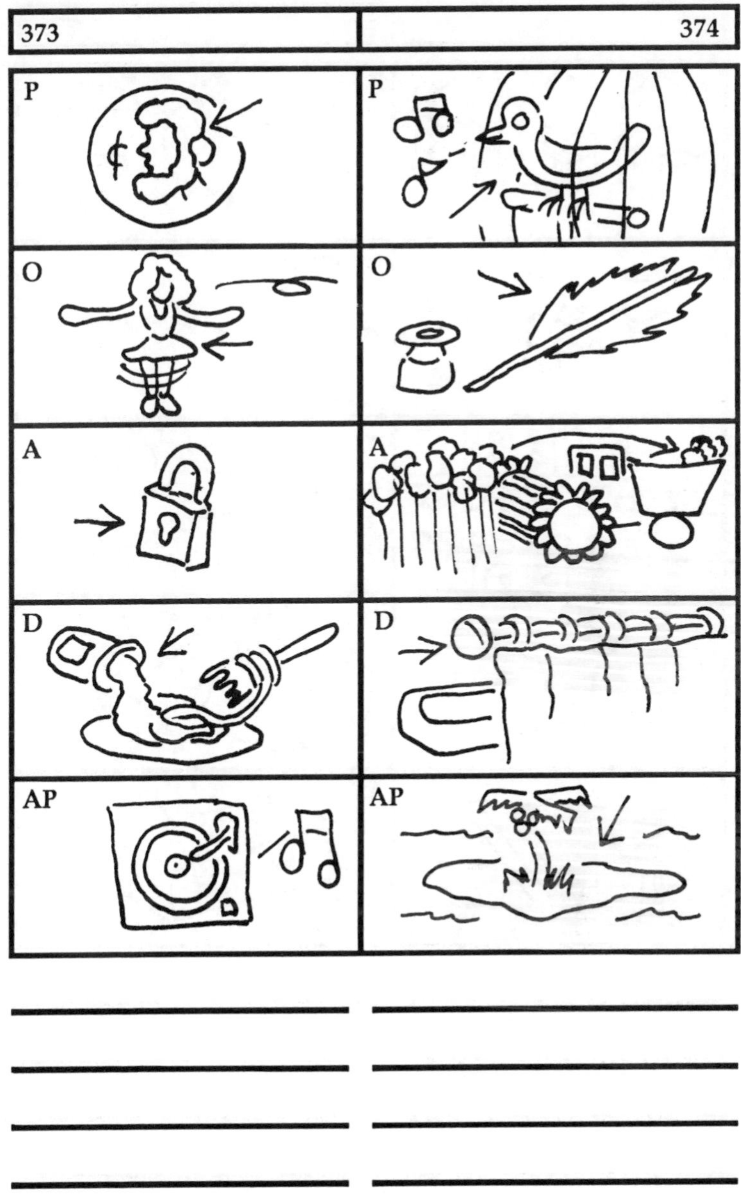

371. Descendant, Stovepipe, Bale, New, Mascara
372. Las Vegas, Telephone Pole, Blend, Young, Earthquake

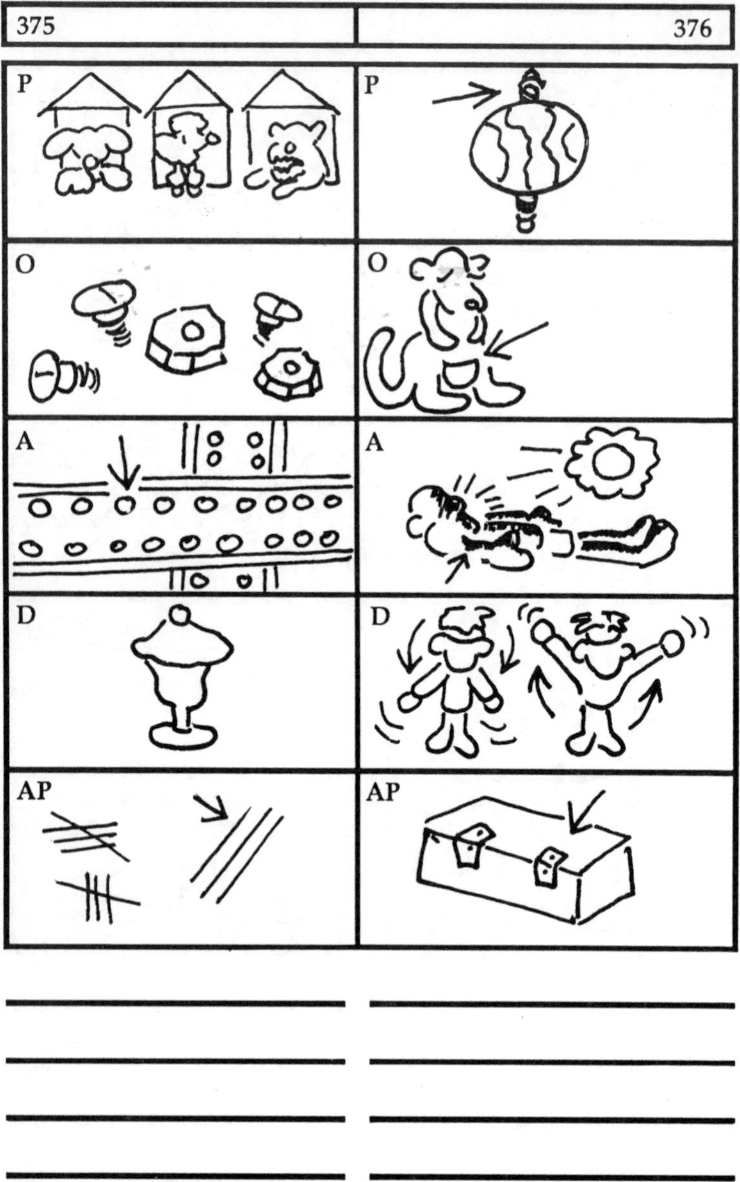

373. Abraham Lincoln, Tutu, Lock, Sauce, Record Player
374. Canary, Feather, Harvest, Curtain Rod, Island

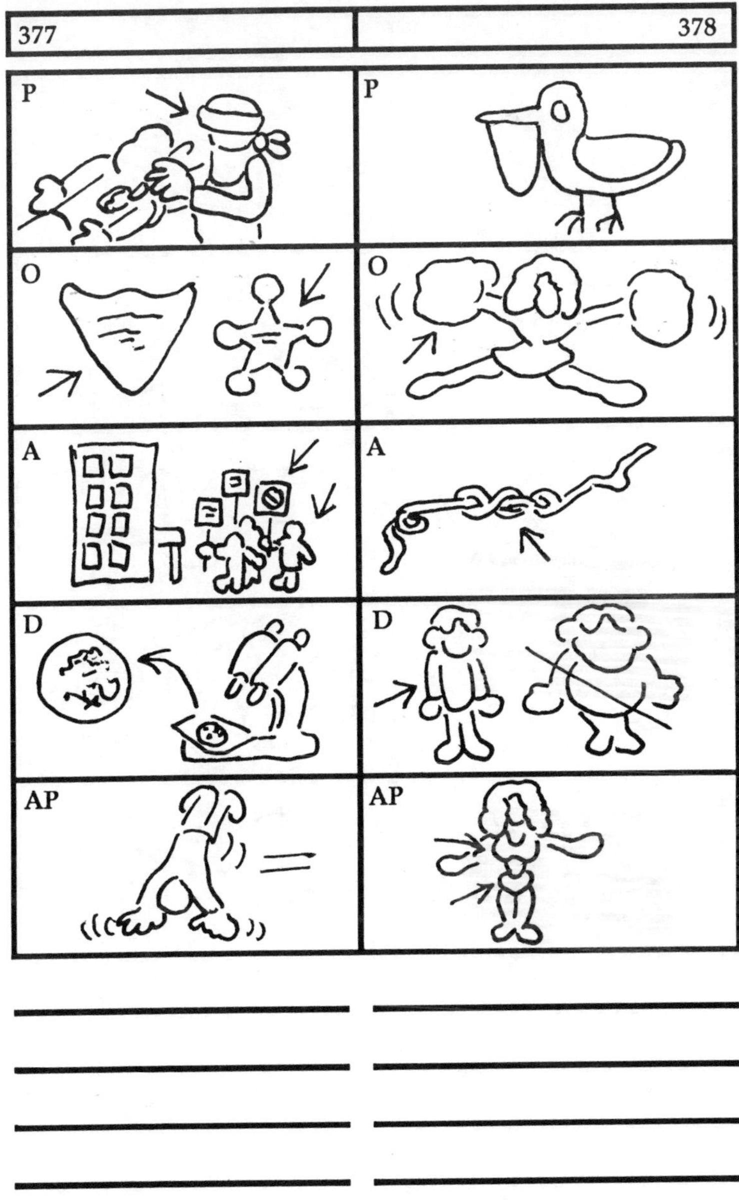

375. Kennel, Nuts and Bolts, Rivet, Sundae, Diagonal
376. North Pole, Pouch, Tan, Exercise, Hinge

377. Surgeon, Badge, Picket, Germ, Handstand
378. Pelican, Pompom, Twist, Skinny, Bathing Suit

379. Al Jolsen, Cupcake, Litter, Campfire, Northeast
380. Creek, Bell Bottom, Mail, Vowel, Spool

381. Skid Row, Clothes, Wave, Nap, Wide
382. Coyote, Brick, Growl, Moose Head, Shell

383. Owl, Tractor, Pounce, Best Seller, Puddle
384. Headache, Hat, Print, Paper, Blowout

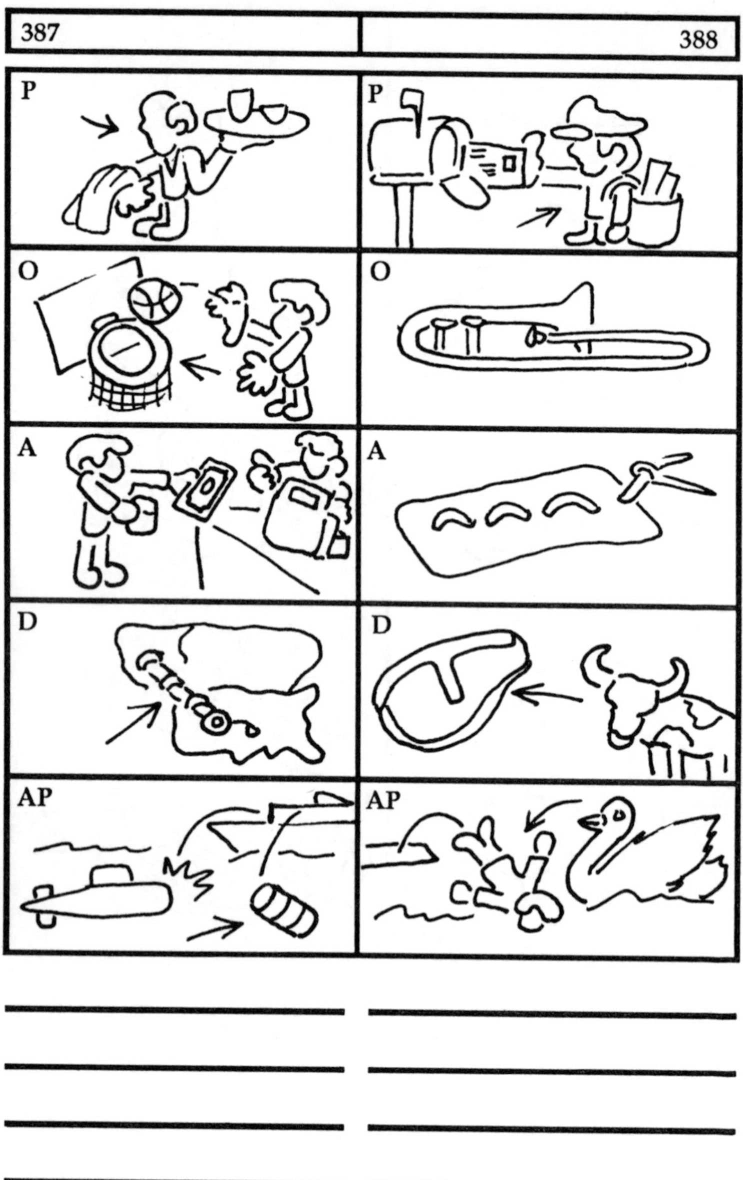

385. North America, Spade, Ban, Nerve, Cloudy
386. Pest, Tool Box, Alternate, Ember, Prize

389	390
P	P
O	O
A	A
D	D
AP	AP

387. Butler, Hoop, Buy, Pipeline, Depth Charge
388. Postman, Trombone, Sew, T-Bone Steak, Swan Dive

389. Zebra, Bean, Spend, Shapely, Sonic Boom
390. Alps, Doorbell, Sunbathe, You, Low

391. Moon, Iceberg, Yell, Blitz, Sideburns
392. Cuba, Notebook, Pound, Polyester, Barstool

393. Basement, Mast, Magnify, Magazine Rack, Earring
394. Tavern, Highchair, Pierce, Paperback, Rainbow

397	398

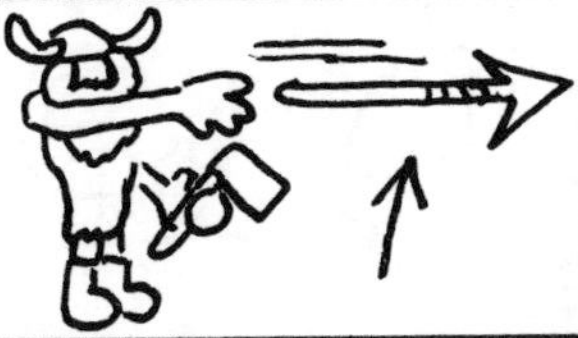

P	P
O	O
A	A
D	D
AP	AP

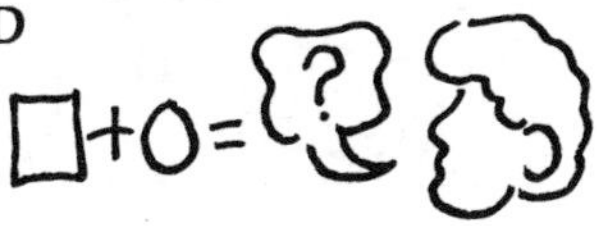

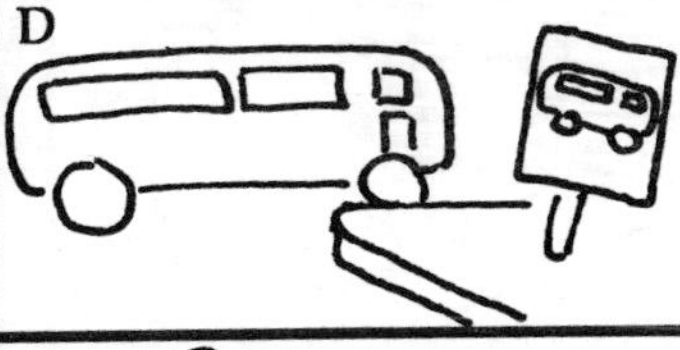

395. Ottawa, Meteor, Cheer, Team, Black Belt
396. Popeye, Shoelace, Fit, Thursday, Haircut

397. Oasis, Fruit, Spear, Guess, Fever
398. Sheriff, Snowball, Flunk, Bus Stop, Snow

399. Butterfly, Cookie Jar, Overturn, Galoshes, Barber
400. Siamese Twins, Prism, Number, Mardi Gras, Stick Figure

401. Muhammad Ali, Helmet, Hitch, Busy Signal, Quotation Marks
402. Arcade, Wading Pool, Trim, Lazy, Sidewalk

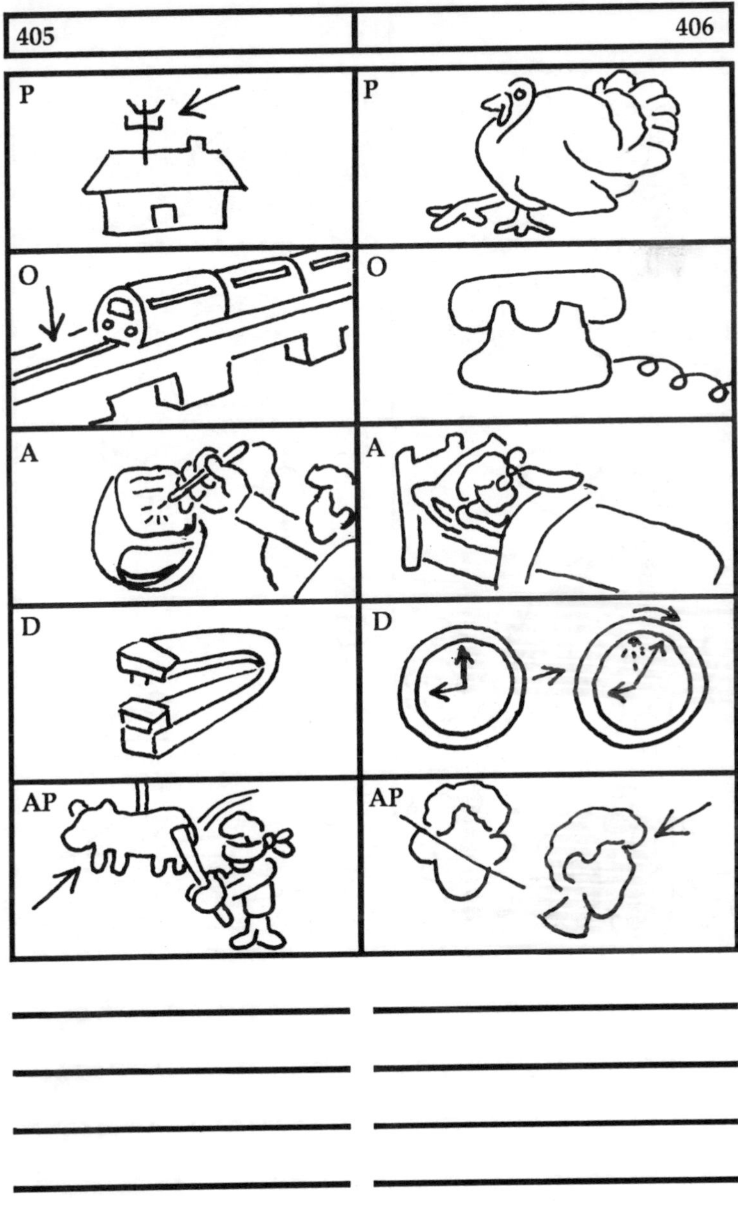

403. Sistine Chapel, Cigarette, Whip, Floor Lamp, Geyser
404. Gladiator, Bulldozer, Juggle, Grounded, Idea

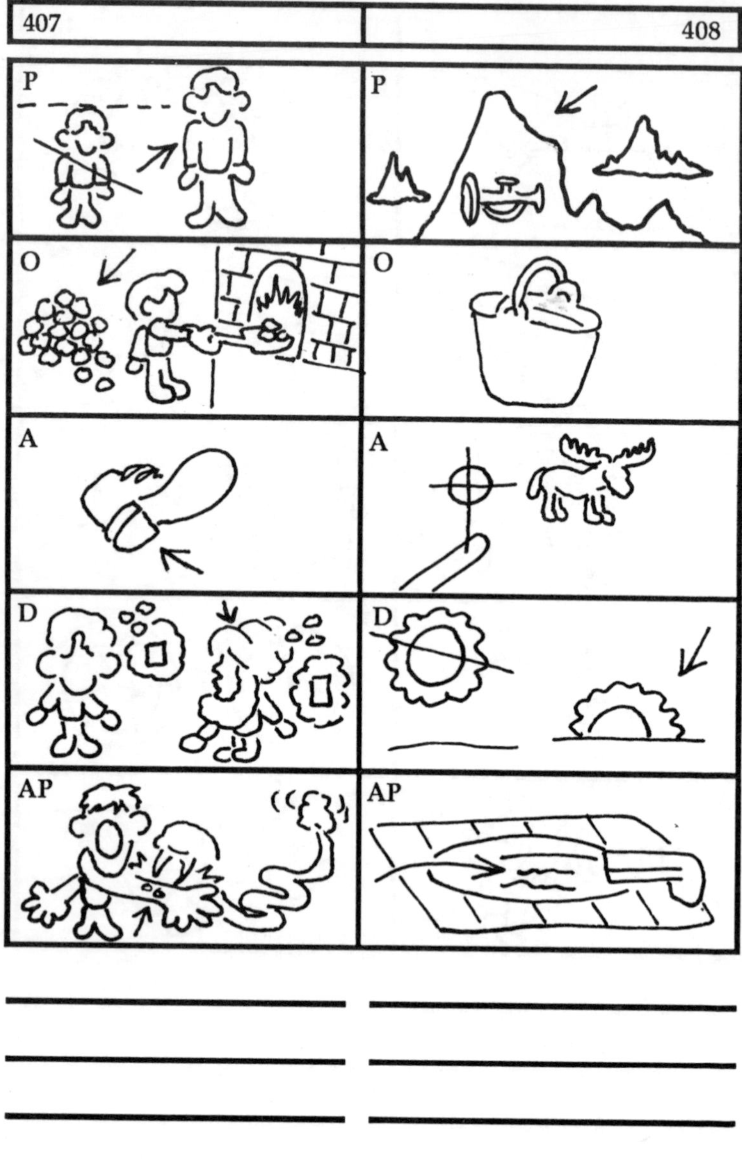

405. Antenna, Monorail, Engrave, Stapler, Pinata
406. Turkey, Telephone, Sleep, Minute, Profile

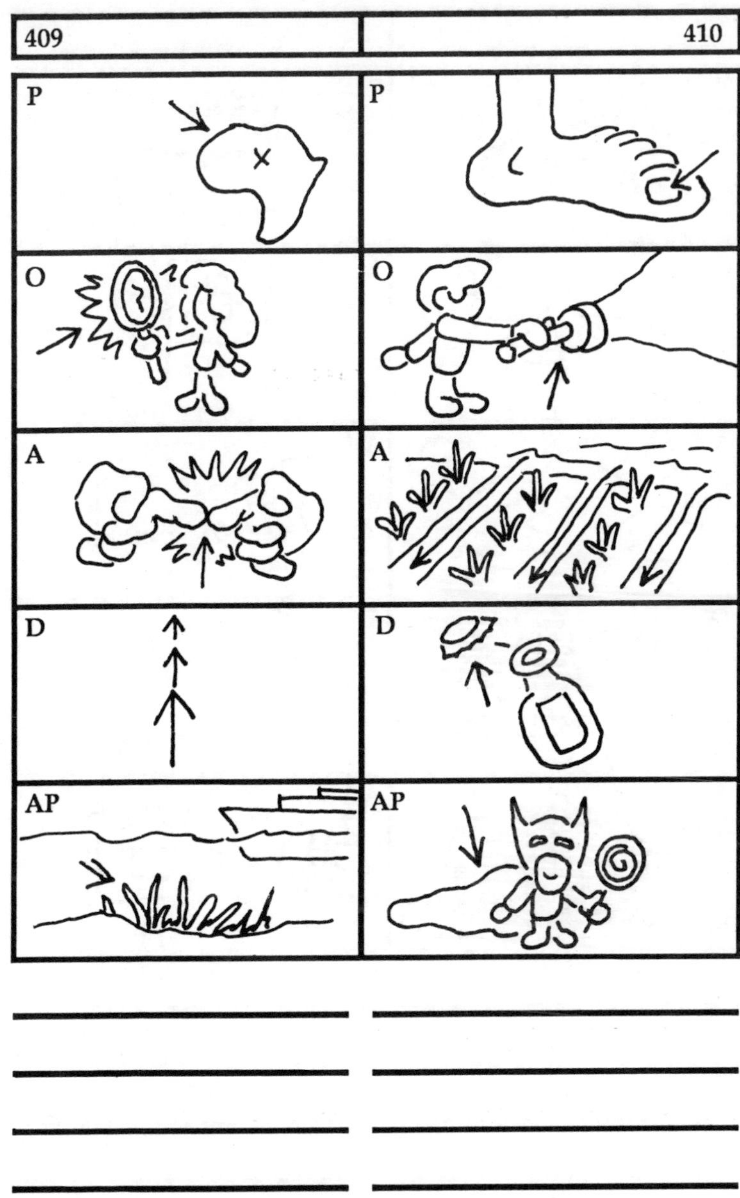

407. Tall, Coal, Heal, Mind Reader, Snake Bite
408. Matterhorn, Pail, Hunt, Sundown, Swimming Pool

409. Africa, Mirror, Touch, Up, Seaweed
410. Toenail, Flashlight, Irrigate, Bottle Cap, Cape

411. Moth, Missile, Heap, Hard-Boiled, Miniature Golf
412. Flying Fish, Wreath, Saw, Cold, Painting

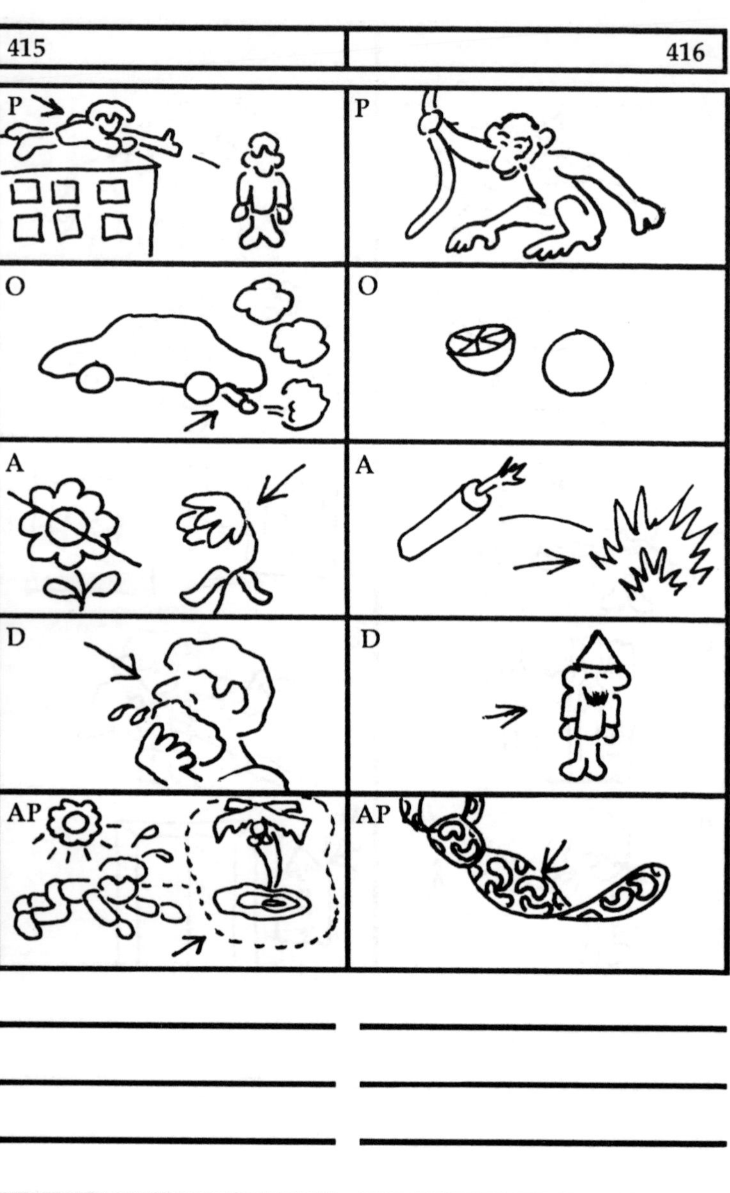

413. Bay, Hot Dog, Slap, Cell, Saber
414. Bison, Yo-Yo, Enlarge, Shot, Lip

415. Sniper, Tailpipe, Wilt, Sniffle, Mirage
416. Ape, Orange, Explode, Oriental, Paisley

417. Zeus, Red Carpet, Catch, Tap Dance, Fret
418. Anchovy, Zipper, Snort, Bakery, Driveway

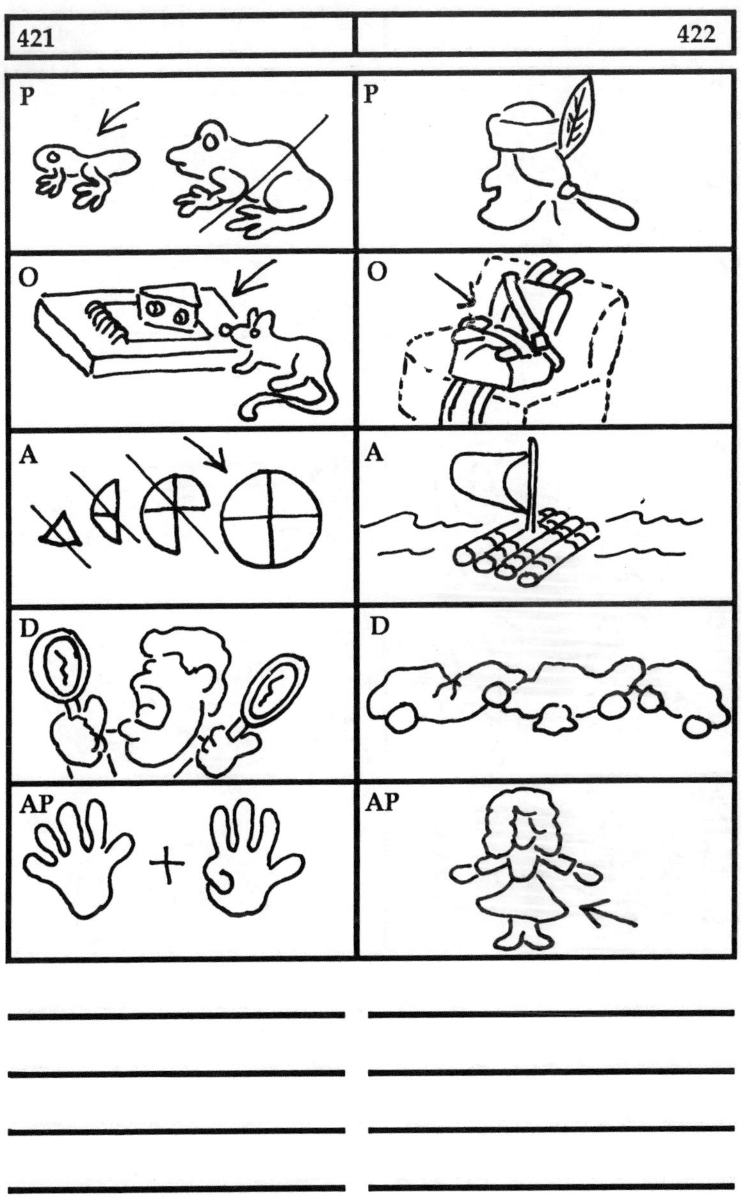

419. Mother-In-Law, Mink Coat, Scuff, Pickup Truck, Haystack
420. Skunk, Bun, Copy, Electric Chair, Clam

421. Tadpole, Mousetrap, Complete, Conceited, Nine
422. Apache, Car Seat, Raft, Pileup, Skirt

423. Knight, Urn, Forge, Sideways, Drag Race
424. America, Carpet, Cruise, Slow-Motion, Udder

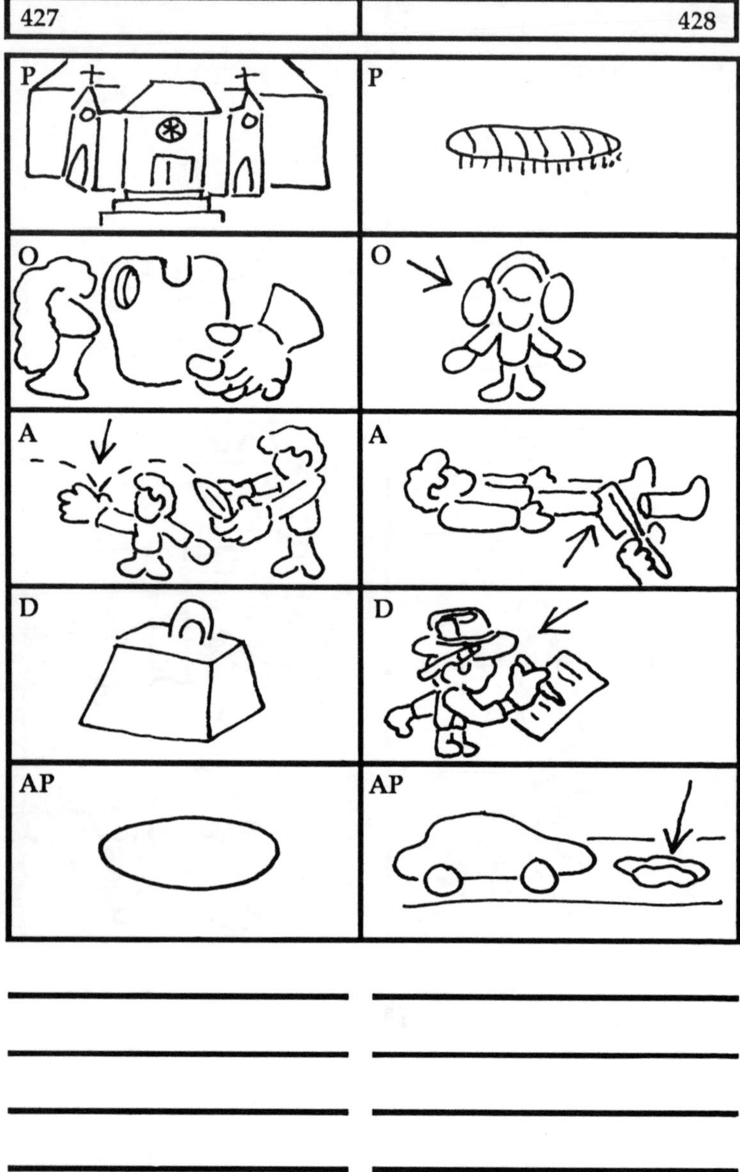

425. Coast, Box Spring, Spit, Black Tie, Joker
426. Niagara Falls, Wallet, Broil, Concrete, Gorilla

427. Cathedral, Armor, Deflect, Ton, Oval
428. Centipede, Earmuff, Amputate, Reporter, Pothole

429. Hair, Tuning Fork, Punt, Blockhead, Shooting Star
430. Chimpanzee, Rose, Capture, Daisy, Carport

431. Cottage, Prune, Scream, Main, Valet
432. Pearl Harbor, Locker, Catapult, Punch Bowl, Halloween

433. Washington, Periscope, Vote, Phone Book, Porcupine
434. Everglades, Dollar, Drip, Passage, Positive

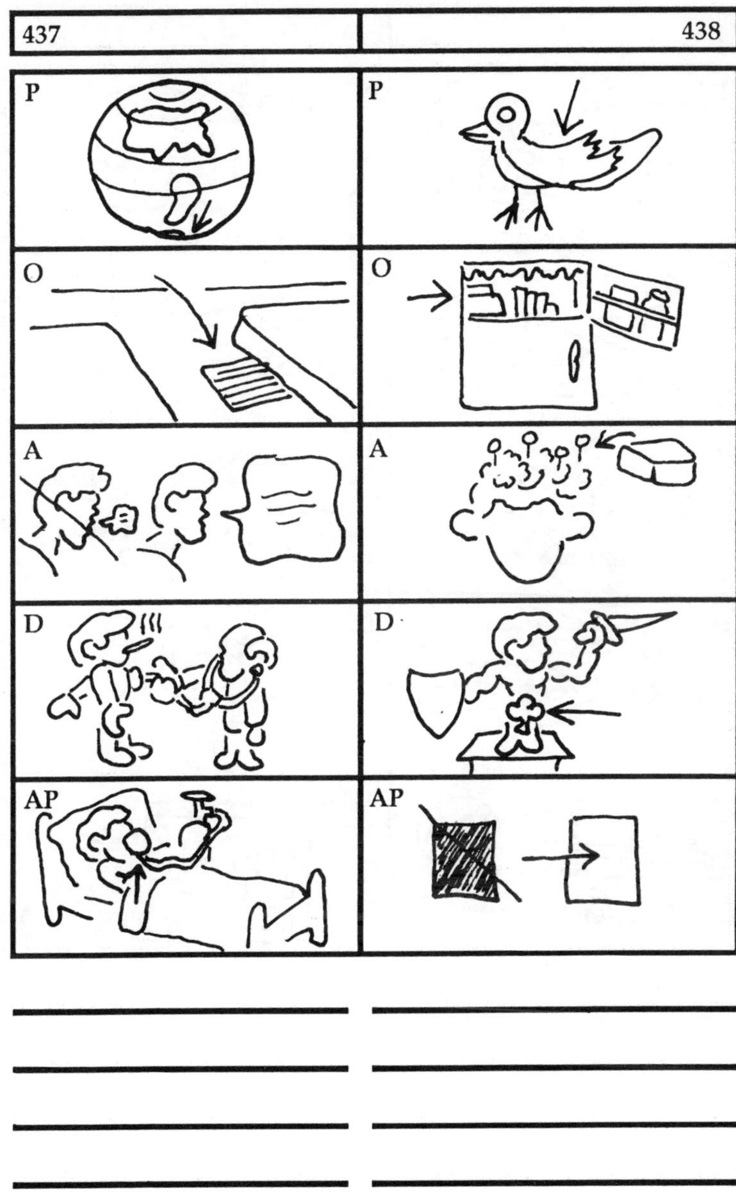

435. Post Office, Cello, Twinkle, Slender, Arrow
436. Houseboat, Ukulele, Injure, Paragraph, Armored Car

437. Antarctica, Gutter, Shout, Physical, Oxygen Mask
438. Wing, Freezer, Brainwash, Fig Leaf, White

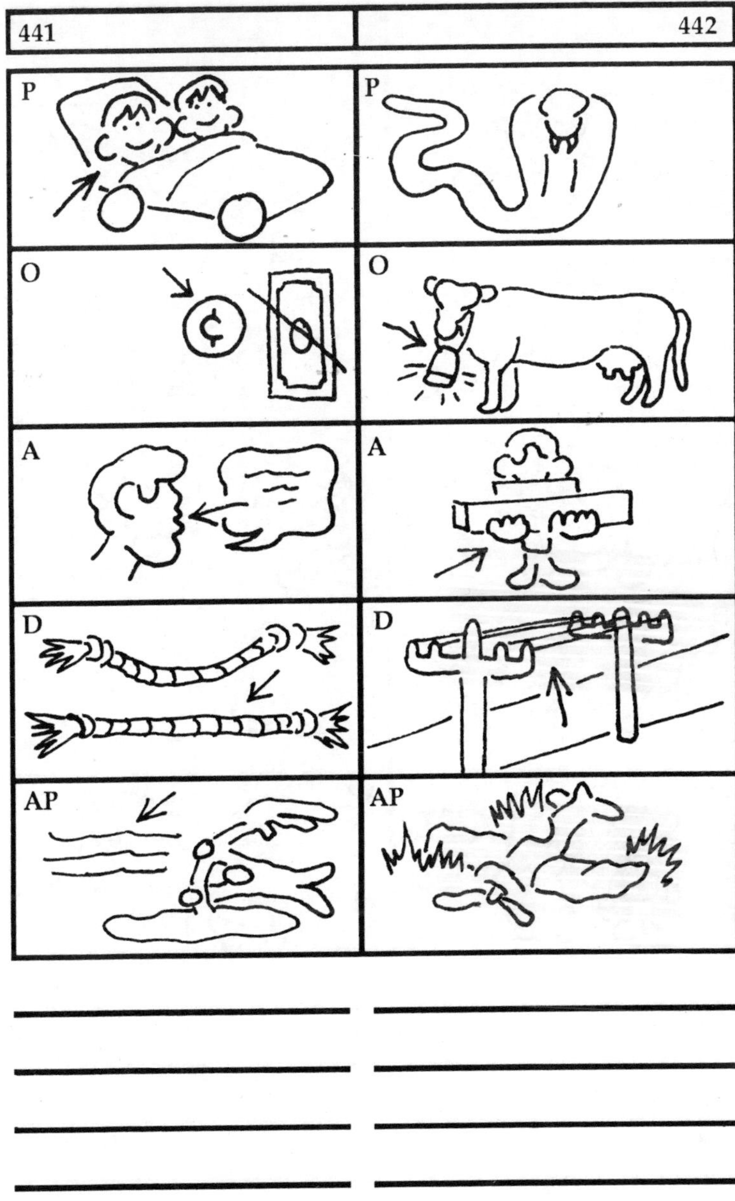

439. Republican, Food, Surround, Obstacle, Cosmonaut
440. Jimmy Carter, Peanut, Drown, Insane, Maze

441. Twin, Quarter, Speak, Tight, Wind
442. Cobra, Cowbell, Carry, Power Lines, Plane Crash

445	446

P	P
O	O
A	A
D	D
AP	AP

443. State, Clock, Roar, Jumpy, Marriage
444. Theater, Stirrup, Chase, Crust, Pegasus

445. East, Gun, Weld, Juice, Fortune Cookie
446. Girl Scout, Socks, Spike, Pharmacy, Ponytail

447. Snail, Smokestack, Bend, Rapids, Zodiac
448. Uncle, Trophy, Fill, Ball and Chain, Noon

449. Eskimo, Hail, Bounce, Beer Mug, Sunburn
450. Bowling Alley, Girdle, Race, Bearskin Rug, Alley

453	454
P	P
O	O
A	A
D	D
AP	AP

451. Hill, Nametag, Jaywalk, Last, Amnesia
452. Camel, Lance, Chauffeur, Surgery, Thorn

453. Black Forest, Glass, Remember, Jewel, Ray
454. Marx Brothers, Coffee Cup, Shoot, Bouncer, Degree

455. Library, Firecracker, Photograph, Blacksmith, Eight Ball
456. Rockies, Lifeboat, Tap, Area Code, Fingernail

457. Chest, Nest, Breathe, Outside, Boxing
458. Antler, Bracelet, Bow, Table Tennis, Wall

459. Poultry, Billy Club, Mow, Taxidermy, Measuring Cup
460. Masseur, Thermostat, Convert, Goal, Root

461. Pool Hall, Coral, Itch, Lockjaw, Lava
462. North Star, Saddle, Mark, Fragile, Part

463. Beady Eyes, Paintbrush, Suck, Station Wagon, Thick
464. School, Oven, Sprain, Concussion, Ghost

465. Charles Lindbergh, Putter, Sweep, Unwind, Lawn
466. Planet, Ejection Seat, Connect, Widow, Trojan Horse

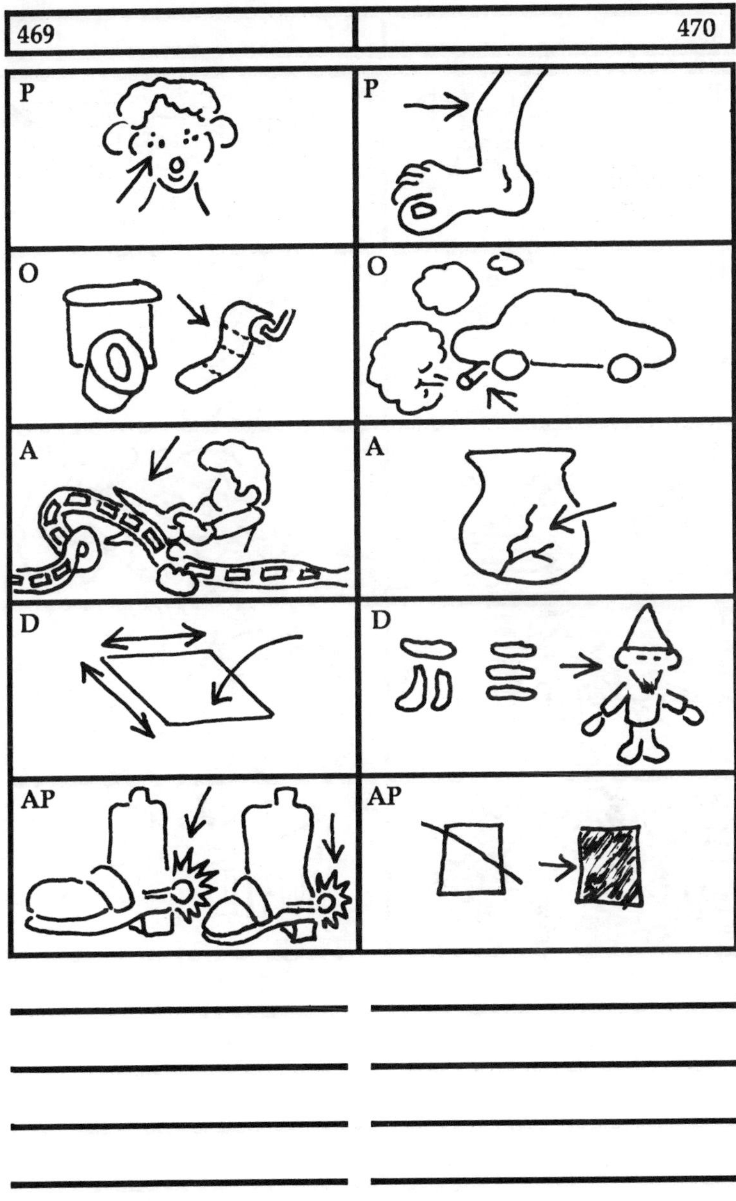

467. Paratrooper, Twig, Answer, Handball, Silhouette
468. England, Apple, Inhale, Past, Corsage

469. Freckle, Toilet Paper, Splice, Area, Spurs
470. Kneecap, Muffler, Crack, Chinese, Black

471. Hair Line, Scarecrow, Unroll, Broken Arm, Odor
472. Vein, Sash, Hallucinate, Saltwater, Drizzle

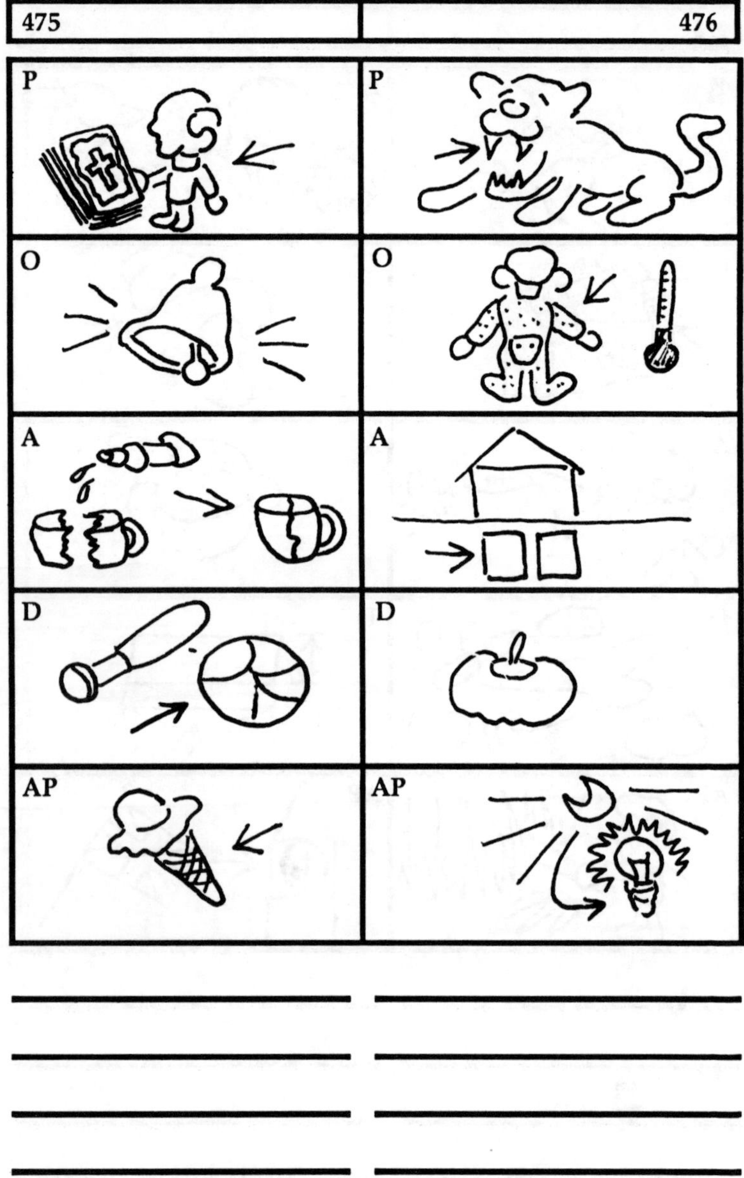

473. South America, Shingle, Pass, Turbulence, Machete
474. Werewolf, Turban, Grin, Length, Big Ben

475. Priest, Bell, Fix, Softball, Icecream Cone
476. Fang, Long Johns, Support, Tomato, Moonlight

479	480

477. Disco, Moccasin, Elevate, Laughing Gas, Third
478. Brother, Razor, Melt, Square Inch, Elevator

479. Waist, Crib, Smother, Second Floor, Sledding
480. Restaurant, Ice Cube, Nod, Internal, Funnel

481. South, Refrigerator, Croak, Sand Trap, Argyle
482. Earlobe, Camera, Beg, Broken, Pillar

483. Panda, Sunglasses, Erase, Handicap, Oar
484. Caddie, Stilts, Count, Capital, Cable

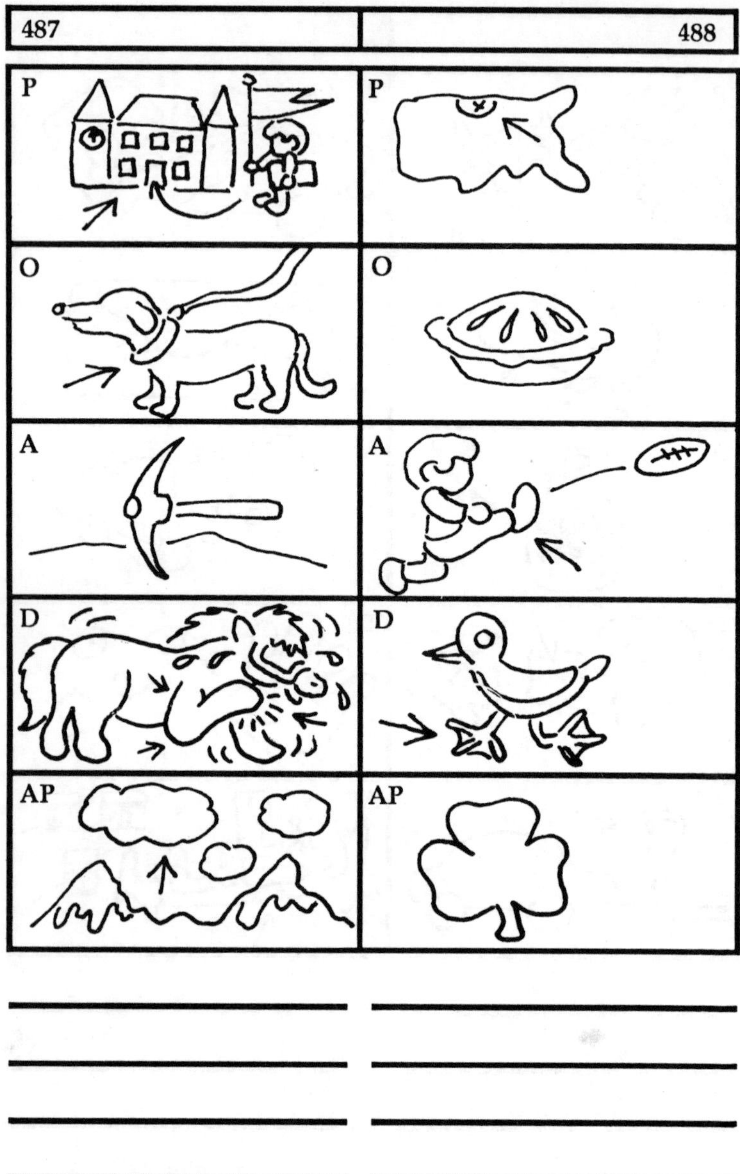

485. Cowgirl, Scarf, Poison, Word, Parking Meter
486. Quadruplets, Envelope, Overheat, Four Eyes, Coma

487. University, Dog Collar, Pick, Lame, Cloud
488. North Dakota, Pie, Kick, Webbed Feet, Cloverleaf

489. Giant, Dessert, Peep, Clothesline, Cuff Link
490. Europe, Ink, Secede, Pansy, Worm

493	494
P	P
O	O
A	A
D	D
AP	AP

491. Painter, Megaphone, Oil, Jealous, Pillow
492. Ostrich, Cleats, Squirt, Life, Skylight

493. Hospital, Pearl, Tunnel, Scenery, Sharp
494. Swan, Plow, Jump, Ouch, Animal

495. Ankle, Egg, See, Forest Fire, One-Way
496. Panther, Anthill, Overlap, Sports, Airport

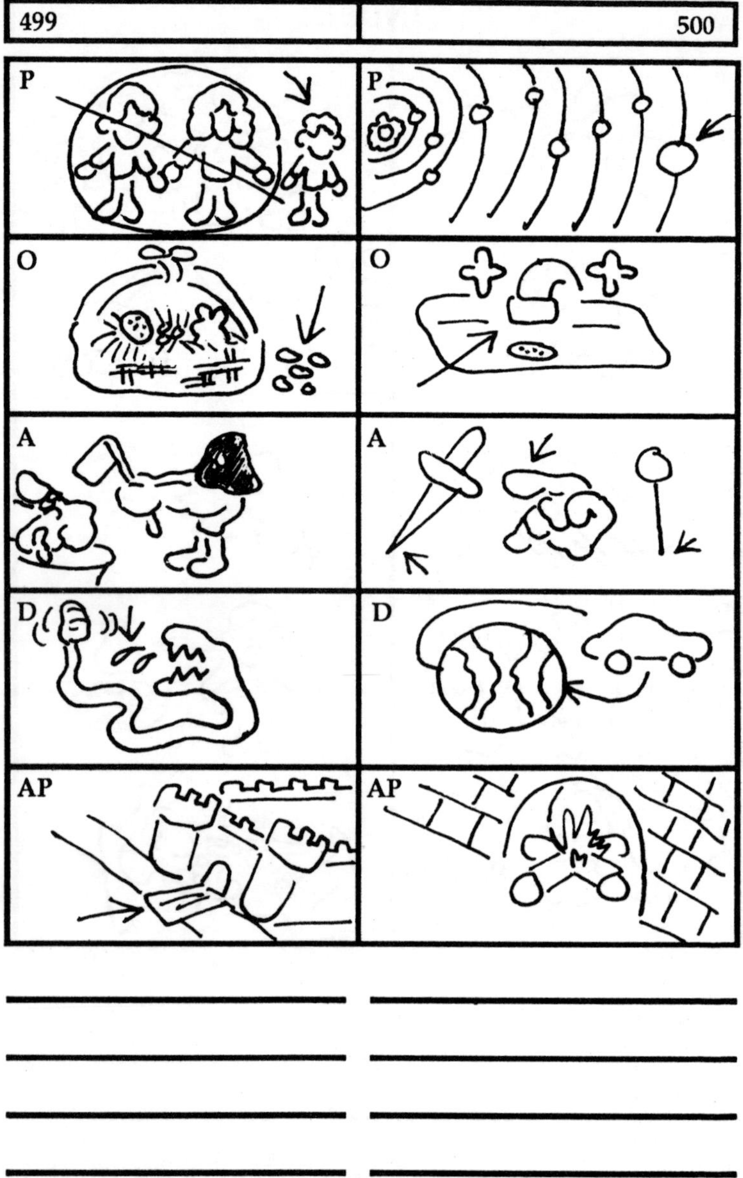

497. Mosquito, Tiara, Scratch, Amusement Park, Weather
498. Bullfight, Wrecking Ball, Cough, Antacid, Pajamas

INDEX

A

Abacus, 302, O
About Face, 38, D
Abraham Lincoln, 373, P
Ace, 11, AP
Adam's Apple, 135, P
Adopt, 10, A
Africa, 409, P
Afro, 156, P
Air, 303, AP
Airplane, 29, O
Airport, 496, AP
Airstrip, 129, D
Alamo, 363, P
Alarm, 17, A
Alarm Clock, 324, O
Alaska, 264, P
Album, 109, O
Alcatraz, 114, AP
Alfalfa, 276, D
Align, 52, A
Al Jolsen, 379, P
Alley, 450, AP
Alligator, 129, P
Almond, 125, O
Alps, 390, P
Alter, 82, A
Alternate, 386, A
Amazon River, 197, P
Ambush, 98, A
America, 424, P
Amnesia, 451, AP
Amp, 147, D
Amtrak, 367, D
Amusement Park, 497, D
Anchor, 300, O
Anchovy, 418, P
Angle, 235, A
Animal, 494, AP
Ankle, 495, P
Answer, 467, A
Ant, 207, P
Antacid, 498, D
Antarctica, 437, P
Anteater, 100, AP
Antenna, 405, P
Anthill, 496, O
Antler, 458, P
Anvil, 44, O
Appendix, 69, AP
Applaud, 19, A
Apple, 468, O
Appliance, 225, D
Approach, 230, A
Apron, 290, O
Arcade, 402, P
Area, 469, D
Area Code, 456, D
Arena, 226, D
Argyle, 481, AP
Arm, 297, P
Armor, 427, O
Amputate, 428, A
Ape, 416, P
Around, 194, AP
Arrow, 435, AP
Art, 110, AP
Art Gallery, 285, P
Ashtray, 82, O
Ask, 334, A
Asteroid, 195, D
Astrodome, 6, P
Athlete, 275, P
Attach, 1, A
Attack, 338, A
Attic, 247, AP
Average, 328, D
Avoid, 341, A
Axle, 252, O

B

Baby, 48, P
Baby Sitter, 103, D
Backache, 44, AP
Back Door, 232, D
Bacon and Eggs, 306, D
Bad, 118, D
Bad Breath, 37, AP
Badge, 337, O
Bag, 231, A
Baggage, 151, O
Bait, 236, A
Bakery, 418, D
Balance Beam, 117, O
Bald, 262, AP
Bald Eagle, 293, P
Bale, 371, A
Ball and Chain, 448, D
Ballast, 266, D
Balloon, 101, O
Ballot, 30, O
Ball Park, 126, P
Ban, 385, A
Banana, 194, O
Banana Peel, 92, D
Bandage, 142, A
Banjo, 251, O
Bank, 43, P
Banner, 245, D
Barbell, 321, O
Barber, 399, AP
Barbwire, 51, AP
Barefoot, 365, AP
Bark, 120, A

Broken Arm, 471, D
Broken Heart, 308, D
Broken Leg, 161, D
Broom, 287, O
Brother, 478, P
Bruise, 191, A
Brush, 280, A
Brush Fire, 35, AP
Bubble Bath, 24, AP
Bucket, 295, AP
Bucket Seat, 127, D
Buckle, 223, A
Build, 78, A
Bull, 32, P
Bulldozer, 404, O
Bullet, 357, O
Bullfight, 498, P
Bull's-Eye, 321, AP
Bum, 44, D
Bumblebee, 153, P
Bump, 2, A
Bun, 420, O
Bunk Bed, 128, AP
Buoy, 335, O
Burn, 34, A
Burnt, 111, A
Burst, 156, A
Bury, 37, A
Bus, 156, O
Bus Station, 234, P
Bus Stop, 398, D
Busy Signal, 401, D
Butler, 175, D
Butler, 387, P
Butterfly, 399, P
Buy, 387, A

C

Cabin, 360, AP
Cable, 484, AP
Cable Car, 7, D
Cable T.V., 46, AP
Cactus, 112, O
Caddie, 484, P
Caffeine, 16, D
California, 120, P
Call, 184, A
Camel, 452, P
Camera, 482, O
Camp, 272, P
Campfire, 379, D
Canada, 195, P
Canary, 374, P
Candle, 213, O
Candelabra, 369, O
Candlelight, 362, AP
Candlestick, 52, D
Candy Cane, 200, O
Cane, 272, O
Cannon, 316, AP
Cannonball, 99, D
Cap, 279, A
Cape, 410, AP
Capital, 484, D
Capsize, 213, A
Capsule, 222, D
Capture, 430, A
Car, 224, AP
Card, 314, O
Card Table, 274, D
Carnation, 246, O
Carnival, 240, P
Carpenter, 250, P
Carpet, 424, O
Carport, 430, AP
Carrot, 326, O
Carry, 442, A
Carry-On, 223, D
Car Seat, 422, O
Cartwheel, 233, AP
Carve, 124, A
Cassette, 278, AP
Castle, 339, AP
Cat, 338, P
Catapult, 432, A
Catch, 417, A
Caterpillar, 330, P
Catfish, 230, P
Cathedral, 427, P
Cauldron, 302, D
Cauliflower, 299, D
Cave, 281, AP
Ceiling, 49, AP
Cell, 413, D
Cello, 435, O
Cemetery, 204, P
Center, 269, A
Centerpiece, 193, D
Centipede, 428, P
Cereal, 270, O
Chain Saw, 104, O
Chain Smoker, 10, D
Chair, 311, O
Chairlift, 31, AP
Chaise Longue, 138, O
Chalk, 196, AP
Champagne, 275, AP
Chandelier, 276, AP
Charades, 202, AP
Charles Lindbergh, 465, P
Chase, 444, A
Chauffeur, 452, A
Cheap, 140, D
Check, 358, A
Checkers, 3, O
Check Mark, 3, AP
Cheek, 164, AP
Cheer, 395, A
Cheerleader, 323, P
Cheeseburger, 76, D
Cheese Grater, 322, O
Cheetah, 337, P
Chef, 100, D
Cheshire Cat, 350, D
Chest, 457, P
Chewing Gum, 20, O
Chicken, 19, P
Chile, 211, P
Chimney, 8, AP
Chimpanzee, 430, P
Chinese, 470, D
Chin-Up, 286, D
Chisel, 237, A
Chocolate Cake, 58, D
Choir, 157, AP
Choke, 205, A
Chop, 247, A
Chopsticks, 320, AP
Christmas, 218, D
Christmas Tree, 361, O
Church, 290, P
Cigarette, 403, O
Civilian, 21, D
Civil War, 141, D
Clam, 420, AP
Clamp, 29, A
Clap, 26, A
Claw, 147, A
Cleats, 492, O
Cleopatra, 345, P
Clink, 206, A

D

E

F

G

H

I

J

K

L

Index

M

N

O

Q

R

Red-Hot, 138, D
Red Wine, 279, D
Redwood, 39, O
Reel, 289, O
Referee, 131, P
Reflect, 310, D
Reflection, 299, AP
Reflector, 273, O
Refrigerator, 481, O
Reindeer, 256, P
Reject, 192, A
Religion, 266, AP
Remember, 453, A
Remote Control, 256, AP
Repairman, 321, D
Repeat, 357, A
Replay, 60, A
Reporter, 428, D
Republican, 439, P
Resort, 109, D
Restaurant, 480, P
Retire, 61, A
Reverse, 194, A
Revolving Door, 345, AP
Rhinoceros, 116, P
Ribbon, 259, O
Ribs, 348, AP
Rich, 108, AP
Richter Scale, 39, AP
Ricochet, 148, A
Ride, 245, A
Rifle, 175, O
Right, 5, AP
Right Bank, 18, P
Right Hand, 83, P
Rim, 181, AP
Rinse, 136, A
Rip, 64, A
Ripe, 30, D
Ripple, 88, A
Rise, 101, A
River, 184, AP
Rivet, 375, A
Riviera, 366, P
Roadblock, 287, AP
Road Map, 365, O
Roast, 117, A
Roar, 443, A
Rob, 110, A
Robe, 253, O
Robin, 241, P
Robot, 116, AP
Rock, 349, A
Rocket, 358, AP
Rockies, 456, P
Rodeo, 286, P
Roll, 202, A
Rome, 311, P
Ronald Reagan, 369, P
Roof, 176, AP
Roommate, 97, P
Root, 460, AP
Rope, 352, O
Rose, 430, O
Rotate, 122, O
Rotten, 84, D
Round, 327, AP
Row, 71, A
Rowboat, 72, O
Rub, 131, A
Rubber, 60, D
Rubber Duck, 13, AP
Rug, 65, O
Ruler, 297, O
Runny Nose, 263, D
Russia, 308, P
Rust, 364, D
Rut, 253, A

S

Saber, 413, AP
Sad, 274, AP
Saddle, 462, O
Safe, 291, O
Safety Pin, 364, AP
Safety Net, 107, O
Sahara Desert, 214, AP
Saint Bernard, 325, P
Sail, 293, O
Sailor, 273, P
Salad, 62, O
Saliva, 75, AP
Saltwater, 472, D
Salute, 44, A
Sand, 69, A
Sandbag, 236, O
Sandstorm, 111, D
Sand Trap, 481, D
San Francisco, 74, P
Santa Claus, 341, AP
Sapphire, 330, D
Sardine, 166, P
Sash, 472, O
Sauce, 373, D
Saw, 412, A
Scale, 134, A
Scar, 348, A
Scarecrow, 471, O
Scarf, 485, O
Scenery, 493, D
School, 464, P
Scoop, 287, A
Scrabble, 98, D
Scramble, 281, D
Scratch, 497, A
Scream, 431, A
Screen, 123, O
Screen Door, 351, O
Screwdriver, 235, O
Scribble, 63, D
Scuff, 419, A
Searchlight, 354, AP
Seat Belt, 339, O
Seattle, 236, P
Seaweed, 409, AP
Secede, 490, A
Second Floor, 479, D
Second Hand, 349, AP
See, 495, A
Seed, 158, O
Seeing Eye Dog, 65, P
Sell, 38, A
Senor, 30, P
Separation, 229, D
Sermon, 238, D
Sew, 388, A
Shadow, 237, AP
Shaft, 192, D
Shag Carpet, 142, O
Shallow, 12, AP
Shampoo, 204, A
Shamrock, 269, AP
Shapely, 389, D
Share, 352, D
Shark, 302, P
Sharp, 493, AP
Shave, 141, A
Shaver, 254, O
Shawl, 227, O
Shed, 221, P
Sheep, 47, P

T

U

V

W

X

Y

Z